JOIN WITH US
BOOK TWO

a collection of stories
for the primary school assembly

JOIN WITH US
BOOK TWO

a collection of stories for the primary school assembly

Jeanne L Jackson

STANLEY
THORNES

First published in 1992 in Great Britain by
Simon & Schuster Education
Reprinted in 1993 (twice)

Reprinted in 1995 by
Stanley Thornes (Publishers) Ltd
Ellenborough House
Wellington Street
Cheltenham GL50 1YW
England

   98 99 00 / 10 9 8 7 6 5

A catalogue record for this book is available from the British Library.

ISBN 0 7487 3471 6

Photoset in 10 on 12pt Times Roman
by Derek Doyle & Associates, Mold, Clwyd.
Printed in Great Britain by T. J. International Ltd.

Contents

Introduction   vii

Acknowledgements   ix

Autumn Term

Week 1	New and old	1
Week 2	Ourselves	6
Week 3	Our talents	12
Week 4	Autumn – Harvest	17
Week 5	Responsibility	25
Week 6	Rules	31
Week 7	Caring	38
Week 8	Treasure	44
Week 9	Advent	52
Week 10	Friends	58
Week 11	Winter	65
Week 12	Christmas	72

Spring Term

Week 1	Each day different	81
Week 2	Persistence	87
Week 3	Families	94
Week 4	Light	99
Week 5	Promises	106
Week 6	Listening	114
Week 7	Food	120
Week 8	Common sense	126
Week 9	Neighbours	132
Week 10	Kindness	139
Week 11	Spring	146
Week 12	Easter	152

Summer Term

Week 1	Thinking ahead	161
Week 2	People	166
Week 3	Feelings	173
Week 4	Partners	180
Week 5	Sharing	187
Week 6	Whitsuntide	193
Week 7	Problems	199
Week 8	Communication	205
Week 9	Summer	212
Week 10	Sports	219
Week 11	Holidays	225
Week 12	Endings	233

Alphabetical index of stories   239

Theme index – other than main themes listed in contents   243

Introduction

Join With Us – Book Two, like its predecessor Book One, contains a collection of 108 primary school assembly stories, divided into three terms, and arranged to follow closely the academic and Christian year. This arrangement, I believe, helps bring unity and continuity to the school, and the assemblies help provide children with a moral code suited to their school community.

Each term is divided into 12 weeks, and each week has three stories based on a single theme. There are hymn suggestions and prayers for those looking for complete, self-contained assemblies. Several stories have additional notes suggesting simply-prepared and easily accessible visual aids. Each story starts and ends in a conversational style which is easily adapted by the narrator.

The stories are drawn from a rich variety of sources – traditional, contemporary, historical, biblical, biographical and seasonal; folk tales, legends, fables, and other faiths; anniversaries and news items. The collection includes much original, specially-written material.

All the stories draw out a moral or teaching point, which reflects the broad traditions of Christian belief. The stories appeal to all children regardless of their background or personal belief. *Join With Us – Book Two*, in common with Book One, does not presume a level of religious commitment from its audience.

The 1988 Education Reform Act presents the challenge of an enhanced flexibility (not an increased rigidity) in the presentation of school collective worship, which must now be 'wholly or mainly of a broadly Christian character'. The ERA emphasises the place of a daily act of collective worship in schools. *Join With Us – Book Two* meets the challenge by presenting three theme-based assemblies each week, knowing that each school will have its individual approach to the remaining two, perhaps via class presentations, singing, or acknowledgement of achievements. *Join*

With Us – Book Two meets the challenge of ERA by presenting a year's assemblies which reflect the broad traditions of Christian belief.

However, above all, I intend and hope that *Join With Us – Book Two* will meet a need in primary schools, by presenting a collection of stories which can be *enjoyed* by both narrator and audience.

Dedicated to Miss Mawer on her retirement from Cobden

Acknowledgements

I wish to express my thanks to
- the children and staff of Cobden Primary School; for their co-operative and enthusiastic participation in all the assemblies, and for continuing to be a source of inspiration and joy.
- Miss Mawer; for her loyalty and support to both Cobden and me, we shall miss her but wish her well in her retirement.
- Val; for her continued and much appreciated support of my writing. Thank you Val.
- And Jim Siller; for his advice on Bible text.

Bible text is reproduced from the Good News Bible © American Bible Society, New York, 1966, 1971 and 4th edition 1976, published by The Bible Societies/Harper Collins, with permission.

Hymn Book References

Reference has been made to the following hymn books:

Alleluya	A & C Black
Carol gaily carol	A & C Black
Come and Praise Vol 1	BBC Publications
Come and Praise Vol 2	BBC Publications
Harlequin	A & C Black
Sing for Joy	EMI Music
Someone's singing, Lord	A & C Black

Several of the stories in this collection are adapted from Aesop. A useful source of further stories is *The Best of Aesop's Fables* by Margaret Clarke and Charlotte Voake, published by Walker Books (ISBN 0 7445 1009 0).

Autumn Term

Biblical references to the theme

Week 1 New and old

'He gives me new strength,
He guides me in right paths.'

Psalms 23:3

'When anyone is joined to Christ, he is a new being; the old is gone, the new has come.'

2 Corinthians 5:17

'What happened before will happen again. What has been done before will be done again. There is nothing new in the whole world.'

Ecclesiastes 1:9

Jim

Week 1 New and old

Welcome to our new school year! It's a new start for everyone today. Even if you were at our school before the holidays, there are lots of new things about today. Everyone is in a new class, you have a new teacher, the teachers have new children; perhaps you already have new books, new pencils and new crayons. You might be wearing some new school clothes, and before the end of the day you might have made a new friend. New starts are exciting!

I have a story for you today about a boy who started a new school year, just like this one, and he found it was a new start in more ways than one.

The boy's name was Jim, and this story starts *before* the summer holidays. Jim went to school every day, just like you do, and he was often very helpful, but . . . sometimes he was naughty. Sometimes he got into trouble, sometimes he didn't work as hard as he could, sometimes he was a bit argumentative, and sometimes he got told off. All in all, he thought of himself as quite a naughty boy.

After the summer holidays Jim went in to a new class. It was quite different from his old one. He had a new teacher, a different classroom, new books, new friends and new work: some of it quite hard.

One day, soon after the start of the new term, Jim's teacher said 'I'm looking for someone very sensible, very reliable, very grown-up, to do a job for me.'

Jim looked round the class and wondered who she'd choose. Perhaps Pria, she was very sensible. Or perhaps Heetesh, he was really reliable. Or maybe Sarah, she was helpful. Or possibly Winston, he was always good.

But the teacher didn't look at any of those children, she looked straight at Jim.

'You're helpful and sensible,' she said. 'You can help.'

Jim turned round to see if she meant someone else behind him, but she didn't.

'Yes. You Jim,' she said.

Jim could hardly believe that he had been chosen. He did the job. It involved taking a message to a class at the other side of school, and bringing back a message and some papers.

The teacher of the other class said how grown-up Jim was. On the way back to his own classroom, Jim met the headteacher in the corridor, and she said how helpful and sensible he was being. He felt so good.

The next day Jim was asked to do another job and he was determined to do it as well as the first. He knew he'd been trusted, and he knew he must show his teacher that she'd been right to trust him. So Jim tried hard, and worked hard.

Soon everyone seemed to be saying 'Isn't Jim helpful. Isn't he sensible and reliable. Isn't he good.'

Jim certainly felt good. He was glad he wasn't naughty and silly any more. It was much more fun being grown up and trusted.

You may think that this is a made-up story; but you'd be wrong! The story is absolutely true. I know, because the boy is here, in this hall! But I've changed the names of all the people in the story, so you won't know who he is. Let's make sure that each one of us tries hard to have a good start to this new school year, so that we can be proud of ourselves and proud of our school.

Prayer
Thank you God for a happy holiday, and for a happy start to the new school year. Help us all to be helpful, sensible and reliable. Help us to do our best in everything.

Amen

Hymn
'One more step'   *Come and Praise* Vol 1

The guardsman and his horse
adapted from Aesop

Week 1   New and old

Lots of things are new at the moment, aren't they? I think many of you will have already made a new friend in your new class. Perhaps you've learned a new game or joined a new team for football or skipping. But I hope you haven't forgotten your old friends. Today's story is about someone who thought he didn't need his old friend any more.

Once upon a time there was a guardsman who looked after his horse very well. The two of them together were the smartest pair in the whole regiment when they went on parade, and that was because the guardsman cared so well for the horse. He gave it the best oats to eat and the cleanest water to drink. He rubbed the horse down when it got wet, and covered it with a thick, warm blanket when it was cold. The guardsman made sure that the horse's stable was dry and clean and warm, and that there was always plenty of good fresh hay.

In return, the horse was always beautifully well behaved for the guardsman. It could understand all the commands that the guardsman gave. It could stand perfectly still when it was on parade, and it could trot at exactly the right speed when they were moving in procession. The horse was never put off by big crowds or sudden noise, and it never kicked its legs or tossed its head like some of the other horses.

The guardsman and the horse were a good team. They trusted each other. They worked well together. They understood each other. They were friends.

And then everything changed.

The guardsman left the regiment and became a farmer instead.

'Well, I'll not need you any more,' he said to the horse, and he put him in a field full of thistles. He gave the horse only mouldy hay to eat and dirty rainwater to drink. At night the guardsman-farmer put the horse in a draughty old tumbledown stable, with mud on the floor and holes in the walls.

The horse was very unhappy. This was no way to treat a friend, even if you didn't need him any more.

And then the letter came.

'Dear Guardsman,' the letter said, 'The Queen is having a special parade and requests all her old guardsmen to be present in the procession. Please attend at 2 o'clock on Wednesday, immaculately groomed and in full dress uniform.'

'Immaculately groomed and in full dress uniform!'

The guardsman went to the wardrobe and got out his uniform. He gave it a quick brush down. He gave the buttons a bit of a polish with a duster, but they didn't shine very well. Then he went outside again to the stable.

'Come on,' he called to his horse. 'I need you.'

He lifted down the horse's saddle and harness, bridle and reins. They all looked very dull and dusty. He rubbed the brown leather of the saddle with the sleeve of his jumper, but it didn't look any better. Then the guardsman looked at the horse. It had thistles sticking to its coat and terrible tangles in its mane and tail. The horse hung its head in shame because it knew it didn't look smart and tidy.

'You'll have to do,' said the guardsman. He threw the saddle on the horse's back and pulled the bridle over its head. Then he put his foot in one of the stirrups and heaved himself up onto the horse's back. He took hold of the reins, sat up as straight as he could in the saddle, and said 'Now then. Walk on. Par . . . ade!'

The horse stood perfectly still. It didn't move forward even one step. Then, slowly, its legs gave way beneath it, and it sank to the floor.

'I can't do it,' said the horse. 'I am too tired. You haven't looked after me and now I am not fit to go in the Queen's procession. I cannot become a proud and beautiful horse again, just because you want me to. You have betrayed my friendship.'

The guardsman climbed down from the horse's back, and neither of them went to the Queen's Parade.

I hope the guardsman tried harder after that, to look after his horse properly. And we must remember not to ignore our old friends just because we don't need them at the moment, or because we have found a new friend.

Prayer
Dear God, thank you for all our friends. Help us to be fair to our friends. Help us not to forget our friends just because we think we don't need them any more. Help us to know that we *always* need friends.

Amen

Hymn
'Give us hope, Lord'   *Come and Praise* Vol 2

Something old, something new   *Week 1   New and old*

'Something old, something new,
Something borrowed, something blue.'
That is an old rhyme that lots of brides say to themselves just before their wedding day. It's supposed to bring them good luck if they wear something old and something new, something that's borrowed and something that's blue. It isn't difficult to gather things together that fit the rhyme. I wonder what you would choose if you had to have all those things.

We wouldn't find it difficult in our school to find something old, or something new, just now; this week especially, we've been thinking about old and new things. I wonder which you like best: old things or new things?

I'm going to tell you about three people I know. One of them is a neighbour, one is a friend, and one is a teacher at our school, but I'm not going to tell you which one; you'll have to work it out for yourself, if you can!

One of my neighbours, who lives by herself, never buys anything new. But she never throws anything away either. She saves everything because it might come in useful. Her house is very cleverly designed to hold all the things she saves – she has cupboards and shelves everywhere. She has a ladder leading into her loft so that she can store things up there, and she never puts her car into the garage, she uses that as an outside storeroom.

If ever anyone needs anything; a bicycle pump or a piece of velvet ribbon, a nail or a bobbin of blue cotton, you can be sure that my neighbour will have it, and she'll be happy to help you.

But, her house isn't as comfortable as it might be because there are old things *everywhere*, and she will never treat herself to anything new, even though it might make her life easier.

In contrast to my neighbour, I have a friend who hates anything that's old. If something becomes even a bit old, she throws it out and buys a new one. Her house is full of lovely new things, but she has no old treasures, or things that have stories behind them, or lovely things that people gave her a long time ago. She throws everything away when it's no longer brand-new, even if it is still working, or still useful or still beautiful to look at.

And then there's the teacher at our school. She likes old things *and* new things. She likes to buy a new car every so often and sometimes she likes to buy new clothes. Not very long ago she had a new kitchen built on to her house. But she also has quite a lot of old things in her home: things with memories and stories to tell, things that might be old but which are still useful. She's very good at looking at something old and turning it into something new. Not very long ago I wanted to throw away an old cupboard because it was scratched and broken, but this particular teacher rescued the cupboard and the next time I saw it, it had new shelves fitted, it had been painted, and had a curtain across the front in place of the broken door. It look very smart now. Another time I was going to throw away some old flat boxes, but this same teacher rescued those and turned them into a very clever filing system for keeping pictures in.

I wonder which person you think is the most sensible with old things and new things? Do you think it's the neighbour who has just old things, or the friend who has just new things, or the teacher who has a mixture of old and new things?

I expect most of you think the same as me. I like to have new things sometimes, but I also like to have things that are old.

Prayer
Thank you God, for old things and new things. Thank you for new books, new clothes and new friends. But thank you as well for the old books we enjoy, the old clothes that are comfortable, and the old friends we know. Help us to know that there is a place for old and new in the world.

Amen

Hymn
'It's a new day'   *Come and Praise* Vol 2

Biblical references to the theme   *Week 2   Ourselves*

'It is your own face that you see reflected in the water and it is your own self that you see in your heart.'

Proverbs 27:19

'I ask God from the wealth of his glory to give you power through his spirit to be strong in your inner selves.'

Ephesians 3:16

The donkey and the dog   *Week 2   Ourselves*
adapted from Aesop

Do you ever wish you were someone else? I think we all think like that from time to time; but it's not very sensible to wish to be another person. After all, if you *did* turn into someone else, you might wish you were *you* again. Today's story is about someone who actually tried to be someone else, but the story doesn't have a very happy ending.

Once upon a time there was a farmer who had a big donkey and a small dog. The donkey had plenty of hay and oats to eat and a good warm stable to sleep in. During the day he worked hard for the farmer, sometimes pulling a cart and sometimes carrying loads of wood or vegetables. But, although he worked hard, he was well looked after and the farmer was never cruel or unkind to him.

The dog was also well looked after, but unlike the donkey, he had no work to do at all. He could play out in the fields during the day if he wanted to, and in the evenings he could curl up on a cushion, or even sit on the farmer's knee and wait to be fed scraps of food from the table.

One day the donkey said to himself, 'This just isn't fair. I don't see why I should have to stay outside in this stable while that dog sits in the house. I wish I could be like him. I wish I could eat all those good things from the table and I wish I could have a fuss made of me like he does. In fact, I wish I *was* him. In fact, I think I *will* be him.'

And without any more ado, the donkey kicked open the door of the stable and galloped round to the kitchen door of the farmhouse. He pushed against the door to open it, and trotted across the kitchen floor.

He pranced into the sitting room and began to do all the things he had ever seen the dog do. He ran round and chased his tail. He lay on the floor and kicked his legs in the air. He swished his long tail from side to side as fast as he could. Then he jumped up and sat on the farmer's knee.

Well! You can imagine what happened. The table fell over and all the dishes and plates, cups and saucers crashed to the floor. A chair fell over. The dog ran away to the corner of the room in fright, and hid under the sideboard. And the farmer's chair tipped over backwards and left the farmer and the donkey sprawling on the carpet.

'You stupid animal,' shouted the farmer, 'What on earth do you think you're doing. Get up. Get off. Get out.' And as soon as the farmer had got himself back on his feet, he bundled the donkey out of the house and into the stable again.

'In future I'll have to lock you in,' said the farmer. 'You're a donkey, not a dog. The sooner you learn that, the better.'

So the poor old donkey, instead of having a fuss made of him as he'd expected, was shut up in his stable without any supper.

'I think I'll stay a donkey,' he said to himself. 'I don't think I'll try to be a dog again.'

I think the donkey was probably happy to be himself again, after he got over the shock of being in so much trouble. And I think the farmer liked him for himself. We must remember to be ourselves, and not try to be someone else.

Prayer
'As long as I live I shall always be My Self – and no other, just me.' Thank you God, for making me, me.

Amen

Hymn

'God knows me'   *Come and Praise* Vol 1

Practical ideas

The quote within the prayer above is from Walter-de-la-Mare's 'Me'. Other poems in the collection which are suitable for reading on this theme include: 'Two deep clear eyes', 'The cupboard' and 'Bunches of grapes'. A collection, *Walter-de-la-Mare poems* is published by Penguin Books.

The lost magic   *Week 2   Ourselves*
adapted from the Amba-Jātaka

The other day I overheard two small children talking in the park. One of them was telling the other one that he'd been to the seaside for his holidays.

'Well,' said the other one. 'I went to America for mine.'

'So what!' said the first one, 'I went to Australia.'

'Well. I've been to the moon!' said the second one.

And at that point I smiled to myself, because of course, he hadn't been to the moon at all. The two children were trying so hard to impress each other about where they'd been, that they were no longer telling the truth.

In today's story, a young man didn't tell the truth about something because he wanted to seem more important than he really was.

Once upon a time a young man went travelling and arrived at a very poor village in India. The people had no money and hardly any food, and they lived in tiny huts made out of sticks and mud. Now it just so happened that the Bodhisatta – who was a very wise man – was living there at that time.

The young man soon noticed that, although there was no fruit growing near the village, the Bodhisatta came home each day with enough fruit for all the people to eat.

'I wonder where he gets it?' said the young man to himself. 'I'll follow him and see where he goes.'

The next day the Bodhisatta set off to the forest and the young man followed. He saw the Bodhisatta walk up to a tree, sprinkle a handful of water on it, and speak some magic words. He saw a shower of leaves scatter to the ground and he saw that wherever a leaf landed, a new fruit tree grew, there, before his very eyes. He saw the fruit trees blossom, then he saw the fruit appear, and grow, and ripen; all in a matter of a minute or two.

The young man was astonished.

The Bodhisatta picked a basketful of fruit and turned to return to the village. As he turned, he saw the young man.

'I've seen you do the magic,' said the young man. 'Will you teach me how to do it?'

'I will,' said the Bodhisatta, 'But the magic will not stay with you. Just you wait and see!'

The Bodhisatta taught the young man the magic spell, and then he said 'But you must always remember to tell the truth if ever you are asked where it came from.'

The young man said that he would, then he said thank you, then he set off on his travels again.

Soon he came to a city and found many people searching for something as though it was lost.

'What are you looking for?' he asked.

'We're looking for fruit,' said a woman. 'The Queen wants fruit and there's none to be found anywhere. The King says there's a reward for anyone who can take fruit to the palace.'

'I can,' said the young man, 'Take me to the King.'

So the young man was taken to the palace and was presented to the King.

'Take me to one of your trees,' said the young man, 'And I'll give you fruit.'

The King took him to the palace garden and stood him in front of a tree. The young man sprinkled a handful of water on it and spoke some magic words. A shower of leaves scattered to the ground and wherever a leaf landed, a new fruit tree grew. The new trees blossomed, the fruit grew and ripened, all in a matter of a minute or two.

The young man picked a fruit and gave it to the King.

'Goodness me!' said the King. 'That's a remarkable piece of magic. Where did you learn to do that?'

But the young man was ashamed to admit that he had learned it from a poor man in a poor village. So instead of telling the truth he said 'Ah! I learned the magic spell from a teacher who is known throughout the world. He is famous in his magic and he asked me to be his special assistant. I worked so well for him that he taught me some of his secrets.'

'I am very impressed,' said the King. 'Show me the magic again.'

The young man sprinkled a handful of water on the tree and said the magic words. A shower of leaves scattered to the ground. Then . . . nothing. And nothing. And nothing.

The King was very angry and sent the young man away, and the young man went back to the village in the forest to ask the Bodhisatta to give the magic again.

But the Bodhisatta said 'No. You pretended to be someone you are not. So? No!'
And the young man went away.

If he'd told the truth and said he learned the magic from a poor man instead of trying to impress the King, I think the story would have had a different ending. Perhaps you could write down what you think might have happened if the young man had told the truth.

Prayer
Dear God, thank you for making each of us different. Help us to know that we don't have to show off to impress people who care about us. Help us just to be ourselves, and to be glad that we are ourselves.

Amen

Hymn
'Simple gifts'   *Come and Praise* Vol 2

The eagle and the jackdaw   *Week 2   Ourselves*
adapted from Aesop

Have you ever been in the middle of painting a picture or making a model, and then looked across at your friend's picture or model, and thought it was better than yours? I think something like that happens to everyone at some time. Perhaps when it happened to you, you felt like copying their work instead of going ahead with your own idea. But I hope you didn't. If everyone always copied everyone else, there'd be no new ideas at all.

Once upon a time a big black bird, called a jackdaw, was sitting on the branch of a tree, watching a flock of sheep in a field. Suddenly, a huge and powerful eagle swooped down from the mountain and grabbed a tiny lamb in its claws. The eagle soared away into the sky still carrying the lamb in its talons.

'Hey, look at that,' said the jackdaw to himself. 'I've never seen anything like that before. It was really clever. I think I'll have a go at that.'

Without thinking any further ahead, the jackdaw flew off his branch and pounced on the back of the biggest sheep in the entire flock. Then, making a great deal of noise with his voice and his wings, he tried to lift himself and the sheep into the air.

Of course he couldn't manage it. He tried again with even more flapping and cawing. And still he couldn't manage it.

By now, his claws had become so entangled in the sheep's thick, woolly coat that he couldn't free himself. And knowing that he was stuck made him flap and struggle and cry even harder. He was making such a hullabaloo and commotion that the shepherd came hurrying over to see what was going on.

'A jackdaw!' he said. 'So, you're playing at being an eagle are you? You think you're going to carry off one of my sheep! Well, you can think again. I'll carry you off instead.' And the shepherd untangled the sheep's wool from the jackdaw's feet and carried him home to show his children.

'He's beautiful,' they said. 'Look at his lovely shiny feathers. What sort of bird is he?'

'He's a jackdaw who thinks he's an eagle,' laughed the shepherd.

'Can we keep him for a pet?' asked the children.

The jackdaw shivered with fright. He was a wild bird, he didn't want to be caged.

'I don't think so,' said the shepherd. 'We'll let him go now you've seen him. I think he's learned his lesson. I don't think he'll try to be an eagle again in a hurry. I think he'll be happy to be himself. He knows he can't become an eagle just by copying one.'

And the shepherd gently threw the jackdaw into the air. He opened his wings and felt the push of air beneath them. He flew up and away, onto the branch of a tree. Then he sat there and watched the flock of sheep in the field below him.

I hope that jackdaw was not silly enough to try being an eagle again. I hope he had learned his lesson, that you can't become someone else just by copying what they do.

Prayer
Help us Lord, to be ourselves. Help us not to copy what other people do, but to think for ourselves.

Amen

Hymn
'This little light of mine' *Sing for Joy*

Biblical references to the theme

Week 3   Our talents

The parable of the three servants.

Matthew 25:14-30

Jesus visits Martha and Mary.

Luke 10:38-42

The computer genius and the dustbinman

Week 3   Our talents

Do you ever think that someone else is much cleverer and better than you, or that you're not as good as they are? I think we all think like that from time to time. Sometimes though, it works the other way, and we feel that we're better than someone else. The thing is, it really doesn't matter who's good at what, because *everyone* is good at something, and *everyone* in the world is important.

Once upon a time there lived a computer genius and a dustbinman. They lived a few doors away from each other down the same street, and when they were boys at school, they'd been quite good friends. But now, they didn't see each other very often; just when they were coming and going to their own houses. In fact, they didn't really like each other any more.

'He just thinks he's clever,' the dustbinman used to say to his wife. 'He just sits there all day long designing stuff on that computer of his. He doesn't even do a proper job of work like me.'

'He's not very clever, is he?' the computer genius used to say to his wife. 'I mean he's not doing an *important* job like me. All he does is shift rubbish about all day. I can't think why I ever used to like him.'

One day the two men met in the street. They couldn't just ignore each other; they had to speak, but somehow even though they didn't say very much, they ended up having an argument. They both stormed away from each other, went into their own houses and slammed their two front doors.

'He's a pain in the neck!' shouted the dustbinman to his wife. 'Well! That's it! I'll have nothing more to do with him. He can empty his own bins in future!'

'The man's insufferable!' yelled the computer genius to his wife. 'Well, I'll show him a thing or two, just you wait and see!'

A week went by and nothing happened. Two weeks went by and the computer genius's dustbins were overflowing with rubbish. Three weeks went by and his garden path was piled high with bin bags. Four weeks went by and he couldn't get into his garden at all for rubbish.

The dustbinman's wife said to her husband 'You can't just leave it there. You'll have to empty his bins. It's your job.'

'I'm not doing it,' said the binman, 'I'm not doing anything for him ever again.'

The next day the binman did his rounds as usual, missing out the house of the computer genius of course, but when he drove his wagon back to the depot, the foreman said 'Wait a minute mate. We've a problem. Something's gone wrong with all the machinery. We can't get rid of the rubbish.'

'What's gone wrong?' said the dustbinman.

'Don't know,' said the foreman, 'Something to do with the computer. We're getting someone in to sort it out.'

'Oh!' said the binman. He had a good idea who the 'someone' was going to be.

Sure enough, a few minutes later, the computer genius arrived at the depot. He walked into the control room and spent a long time with the controlling computer.

The depot men stood around and waited.

After a couple of hours the computer genius came out of the control room and had a word with the foreman, then he came out into the depot yard.

'It's fixed,' was all he said to the men.

Soon the machinery was all-systems-go again and the binman was able to unload his wagon and set out again to collect more rubbish.

The first house he went to was, of course . . . the computer genius's house.

'I'm sorry,' he said.

'I'm sorry too,' said the computer genius. 'I think I need you as much as you need me. We've all got a job to do haven't we, and I think all our jobs are as important as each others'.'

And they shook hands on it.

In our world and in our school we're all good at something, and we all have a job to do. We all need each other and we all need to work together to make our school a good place to be.

Prayer
Dear God, help us to know that we all need each other. Help us to know that we are all good at something. Help us to use our talents sensibly.

Amen

Hymn
'The best gift'   *Come and Praise* Vol 1

The two brothers

In our last assembly we heard about two people who were good at very different sorts of jobs. Today I have a story about two brothers who were good at the same thing, but one of them gave all he had to help the other one.

Many years ago in Germany, there lived two brothers who were both very poor. Both of them were good at painting and drawing and both of them wanted to be artists. But, to be an artist, you had to go to art school to be trained, and while you were being trained you were not paid any money. So it seemed impossible for either of them to go. They simply couldn't afford it.

Then the older brother, who was called Franz, had an idea. It was a very kind idea, and a very unselfish idea.

'Albrecht,' he said. 'I know you are younger than me, but your talent is greater than mine; you are a better artist. I will go out to work as a labourer, doing odd jobs for people, and I will earn enough money for us to live on, while you go to art school and train to be an artist. Then, when you are successful and are earning money by selling your paintings, you can pay for *me* to go to art school and I can have *my* training.'

'But what labouring jobs can you do?' asked Albrecht.

'I can build walls, or mend furniture, or do any kind of odd jobs,' said Franz.

'It'll be hard work,' said Albrecht.

'I know,' said Franz, 'But this way we can both go to art school in the end.'

So it was settled. Franz worked as a labourer, and very hard work it was too. Albrecht went to art school and trained to be an artist.

After a long time Albrecht sold his first picture. Then he sold another one. A few years later he sold another and then another. People began asking him to paint pictures especially for them, and eventually he became famous for his paintings.

One day he stood in front of Franz and said 'Thank you. If it hadn't been for your idea and all your hard work, this wouldn't have been possible. Now it's your turn. *I* will look after both of us and *you* can go to art school.'

But Franz said not one word.

He just held up his hands for Albrecht to see. His hands were gnarled and bent, twisted and painful. His fingers were swollen and sore because of all the hard work he had done, mending gates, building walls and repairing furniture. He could no longer hold a pencil or paintbrush. His hands were the hands of a workman, not the fine hands of an artist.

'Franz,' said Albrecht, 'I didn't know. I never noticed.'

Then Albrecht said, 'Stay there.' And he brought paper and pencil and drew a beautiful portrait of his brother's hands.

When the drawing was finished everyone said how wonderful it was, how full of love it was, and how remarkable it was.

People still say those things today, four hundred years after the picture was drawn, because it has become one of the most famous pictures in the world. Albrecht's surname was Dürer, and he called his drawing of Franz's hands 'The praying hands'. In the picture we can see how much Franz must have loved his brother, to give up his own dream of becoming an artist, so that Albrecht could become one.

We can't all become famous artists, but we can all do our best in everything we do.

Prayer

Help us, God, to do our best in everything we do. Help us to know that we all have a part to play and that all the parts are important.

Amen

Hymn

'I belong to a family'   *Come and Praise* Vol 1

Practical ideas

This assembly would be incomplete without showing the children Albrecht's drawing of Franz's hands. The drawing is reproduced in many books, and is also available as a postcard or poster, by mail, from Devotion, 19 Merrion Street, Leeds LS2 8JE. The drawing might inspire the children to try their own observational drawings of hands. What they see may be quite different from what they think they see, particularly if they are first asked to draw what they imagine a hand to look like.

The bumble bee   *Week 3   Our talents*

This week we have been thinking about everyone having his or her special talent and everyone being good at something. Sometimes, though, it's better not to think about whether we're good or not, but just to get on with it!

Once upon a time there was a fat and furry bumble bee who lived in a garden. She was ready to choose an underground site for her nest. She searched the garden and found an old mouse hole that was exactly right for her. She pulled in some bits of grass, collected some pollen on her hind legs and put that on the grass, then laid her eggs on top of the pollen.

A few days later the eggs hatched out into grubs and began to eat the pollen that the bumble bee had put into the nest. The grubs were so greedy that the pollen was quickly eaten and the bumble bee had to fly out and collect more.

She was soon busy all day long collecting pollen on her hind legs and flying back to the nest with it to feed the growing grubs.

While she was doing this, two men, who happened to be aeroplane designers, were sitting in deckchairs watching her.

'Do you know,' said one man, 'It's a fact that bumble bees have bodies that are too heavy for their wings?'

'I know,' said the other. 'According to everything we know about flying, bumble bees cannot fly at all! Their wings are too small to carry them.'

'What's more,' said the first man, 'scientists have worked out that bumble bees carry half their own weight in pollen on their hind legs. Just imagine! Half their own weight again.'

'It's true,' said the second man, 'According to statistics, they can't fly. It's impossible for them even to get off the ground.'

'Absolutely impossible,' agreed the first man.

And they carried on watching the bumble bee, who was, of course, flying backwards and forwards to and from her nest.

Luckily, no-one had told the bumble bee that it was impossible for her to fly. No-one had told her that her wings were too small, or that her body was too large. And no-one had told her that the pollen she carried on her hind legs was too heavy for her.

So she continued, all day long, to fly backwards and forwards with pollen to feed the grubs in her nest.

Bumble bees work hard all summer, laying batch after batch of eggs, then feeding the grubs with pollen from the flowers. It's true that some scientists say that they shouldn't be able to fly at all. But let's make sure we don't tell the bees, or they just might believe what they are told!

Next time you think you're not clever enough to do something – have a go. You might surprise yourself, and other people too.

Prayer

Dear God, please help us not to give up if we think something is going to be difficult. Help us to remember that if we *think* we can do a thing, often we *can* do it.

Amen

Hymn
'The best gift'   *Come and Praise* Vol 1

Biblical references to the theme   *Week 4   Autumn harvest*

'So then, obey the commandments . . . If you do, he will send rain on your land when it is needed, in the autumn and in the spring, so that there will be corn, wine, and olive-oil for you.'

Deuteronomy 11:13-14

'And God, who supplies seed to sow and bread to eat, will also supply you with all the seed you need and will make it grow and produce a rich harvest from your generosity.'

2 Corinthians 9:10

Harvest Festival: Bread   *Week 4   Autumn harvest*

Can you think of a food that is eaten in just about every country in the world, and yet looks and tastes different in each country?

This food I'm thinking of comes in different shapes, sizes and tastes in this country. We buy it in shops and supermarkets; we can buy little ones or big ones. We can buy it ready baked or frozen, sliced or unsliced, plain or fancy.

Yes, you've got it – it's bread.

This morning the children in class five are going to tell you about bread.

Child 1 Did you know that people all over the world eat some kind of bread?

Child 2 Did you know that bread helps us to grow strong and healthy?

Child 3 Did you know that there are lots of different kinds of bread, and that it comes in all sorts of shapes and sizes?

Child 4 This is a baguette from France.

Child 5 This is pitta bread from Israel.

Child 6 This is a sliced loaf from England.

Child 7 This is pumpernickel bread from Germany.

Child 8 These are bagels from Israel.

Child 9 These are chappatis from India.

Child 10 This is a pizza base from Italy.

Child 11 This is challah bread from Israel.

(We obtained the various breads from our local supermarket. The list can be varied depending on local availability of the different breads.)

Child 1 Did you know that all these different breads are made from dough? Dough is a mixture of flour and water.
Child 2 Did you know that sometimes yeast is added to the dough? It makes the dough rise. The dough is usually cooked in an oven.

(Here, bread in various stages of its manufacture could be shown to children, together with separate flour, water and yeast. We have found the 'Blue Peter' approach successful, using the 'here is one I made earlier' method.)

Child 1 Do you know when bread was invented?
Child 12 A hundred years ago?
Child 13 Two hundred years ago?
Child 14 Five hundred years ago?
Child 1 No! Twelve thousand years ago!
Child 15 How was it invented?
Child 2 Some people in a village in Turkey found the seeds of some wild grass, and ground the seeds into flour. They mixed the flour with water to make dough, and spread the dough on the hot stones, to bake in the sun.
Child 3 Later, some people in Egypt put yeast in the dough, and it made the dough rise.

Child 1 Did you know that here in England, two hundred years ago, bread became too expensive for ordinary people to buy? A loaf of bread cost as much as a man's wage.
Child 16 Did all the people starve?
Child 3 No. A man called Richard Cobden changed the law, to make corn cheap again. Cheaper corn meant cheaper flour which meant cheaper bread.
Child 17 I'm glad we can afford to buy bread now.

Hymn
'When the corn is planted'   *Someone's singing, Lord*

Child 18 (*to shopkeeper*) Please may I have a loaf of bread? (*buys bread*) Thank you for my loaf of bread.
Shopkeeper (19) Don't thank me, I only sell the bread. You must say thank you to the van driver.
Child 18 (*to driver*) Thank you for my loaf of bread.

Driver (20) Don't thank me. I only delivered the bread. You must say thank you to the baker.
Child 18 (*to baker*) Thank you for my loaf of bread.
Baker (21) Don't thank me. I only bake the bread. You must say thank you to the miller.
Child 18 (*to miller*) Thank you for my loaf of bread.
Miller (22) Don't thank me. I only grind the flour from the grains of wheat. You must say thank you to the farmer for growing the corn.
Child 18 (*to farmer*) Thank you for my loaf of bread.
Farmer (23) Don't thank me. I only planted the seeds and collected the harvest when it was ready. You must say thank you to the seeds.
Child 18 (*to seeds*) Thank you for my loaf of bread.
Seeds (24-27) Don't thank us. We couldn't grow without help from the soil and sun and rain. You must say thank you to them.
Child 18 (*to soil, sun, rain*) Thank you for my loaf of bread.
Soil, Sun, Rain (28-30) Don't thank us. You must say thank you to the one who made us. You must say thank you to God.

Prayer

Thank you God for the rain and the sun.
Thank you for the earth and the sky.
Thank you for the seeds that grow and the farmers who help them.
Thank you for the millers who make our flour.
Thank you for the bakers who bake our bread.
Thank you for the delivery people and the shopkeepers.
Thank you God for my loaf of bread.

Amen

Hymn

'The farmer comes to scatter the seed' *Someone's singing, Lord*

Practical ideas

We had bread in its various stages of manufacture, ready to show the children in assembly. With careful timing, a loaf was ready (we had a cooker in the hall) at the end of the assembly, and this was produced, golden and smelling delicious, to the delight of the children. Had the cooker not been available, we would have asked the kitchen staff to help by bringing in a newly baked loaf.

In the second part of the assembly, children dressed up as the various characters. They augmented their costumes with paintings and models.

A display of books and pictures about bread was prepared. Particularly useful were:

Bread by Dorothy Turner, published by Wayland (ISBN 1 85210 252 7); and *Thank you for a loaf of bread* by Patricia & Victor Smeltzer, published by Lion Books (ISBN 0 85648 241 2) from which the second part of the above class assembly was adapted.

Skip-a-snack   *Week 4   Autumn harvest*

The other day I was watching television when a short film about children in Africa came on. The children were thin and poor. They had few clothes and little food. Some of them were very ill indeed and probably died only a short time after the film was made. A doctor was explaining that it was very difficult for her and her nurses to care for the children because they had hardly any medicines to give them. Sometimes there was so little food, that mothers had to decide which of their children to give the food to. It must have been very hard for them.

And then I thought of you, the children in our school. Sometimes I've heard you say – 'I'm starving!' – when you've been ready for your dinner, but I know that no-one here has ever been really and truly starving. We are very lucky because we have plenty of food.

Some children in a school I know decided to try to help some hungry children in Africa. This is how it happened.

One day Princess Anne went to a special lunch in London. She had been invited to go to the lunch to speak to people afterwards about her work as President of the Save the Children Fund. Now everyone knows that when a member of the Royal Family is invited to lunch, a very special meal is prepared. And everyone knows that very special meals cost a great deal of money.

Princess Anne of course, knew that too. She also knew that the amount of money that would be spent on the lunch, would buy a lot of meals for children in Africa. So she said to the organisers of the lunch – 'Skip lunch, feed a child'. She meant 'Don't spend a lot of money on a special meal for me; give the money to the Save the Children Fund instead.'

That evening all the television news programmes showed Princess Anne at the lunch, and they showed her giving her speech and saying 'Skip lunch, feed a child.'

Lots of children at Cobden Primary School saw Princess Anne on the news, and the next day when they came to school, they asked if they could do as she had asked.

'What do you mean?' said their headteacher.

'We want to do without our lunch so that we can send our dinner money to the Save the Children Fund.

'Well,' said the headteacher, 'That's not as easy as it sounds. Growing children need to have their lunch. They shouldn't go all day from breakfast until tea, without anything to eat. Perhaps we could go without something else instead. What do you think?'

The children thought. They wondered about giving up their pocket money for a week; they thought they could go without sweets at the weekend; but they really wanted to do what Princess Anne had suggested, so those ideas weren't really what they wanted.

'I know!' someone said. 'We could change it from "Skip lunch", to "Skip a snack". We could go without our apples and crisps at playtime, and bring the money that we would have spent, and send it to Princess Anne to help the children in Africa.'

'Now that's a good idea,' said the headteacher. 'We'll tell everyone else about it in assembly tomorrow.'

So they did. They explained what they wanted to do and asked everyone else in the school what they thought. Everyone, from the smallest children to the oldest children, thought it was a good idea.

They decided to 'Skip a snack' the following Friday. The children told their mums and dads about the plan, and they began to put aside the money they would have spent on an apple or a bag of crisps for playtime. They didn't *have* to join in; no-one said they *must* join in; they could help if they wanted to.

Friday morning came. At the beginning of playtime the teachers said 'It's playtime, but if anyone wants to give their snack money to help the children in Africa, you can go to the hall now, before you go out to play.'

In no time at all the school hall was full of children. No-one was silly or noisy. Everyone was helpful and sensible. It turned out that every single person in the whole of the school had decided to help. A long queue stretched around the hall in a wiggly line. The children waited quietly in the queue until it was their turn to walk past the table. On the table was a big glass jar into which they dropped their money. And in a few minutes the jar was full to the top.

When the money was counted, there was more than 70 pounds to send to the Save the Children Fund.

The children wrote a letter to Princess Anne to tell her that it was because of what she'd said that they'd decided to help the children of Africa.

One week later an official-looking letter arrived at the school. It had no postage stamp on it, but it had a London postmark and an interesting blue circle with the letters E.R. and a crown in it. The children guessed where it was from. You've probably guessed too. It was from Princess Anne, saying thank you to the children for trying to help others who were less fortunate than themselves.

The children at that school were ordinary children. They were not rich children who had a lot of money. It was good that they all wanted to join in and help, wasn't it?

Prayer
Thank you God for the food we have every day. Thank you for our breakfasts and dinners and teas. Thank you for fruit and crisps and sweets. Thank you for ice-cream and chocolate and pop. Help us to remember that not all children have as much to eat as we do. Help us to help them if we can, and help the world leaders to share out the food of the world as fairly as is possible.

Amen

Hymn
Thank you, Lord   *Come and Praise* Vol 1

Practical ideas
If this assembly should inspire others to help the Save the Children Fund, its address is Mary Datchelor House, Grove Lane, London SE5 8RD (Tel: 071 703 5400). In addition to overseas work, the organisation runs playgroups in the UK and works with under fives, children in hospital and residential care, travelling children, youth clubs and community centres.

Corn dollies   *Week 4   Autumn harvest*
inspired by 'Lark Rise to Candleford' by Flora Thompson

Have you seen one of these before? (*Show a corn dolly.*) Do you know what it is? It's a corn dolly. Nowadays these are used just for decoration. You sometimes see them for sale in craft shops in the country. That's where I bought this one. If you have some art straws and some ribbon in your classroom, you could try making a corn dolly of your own after assembly.
     Many years ago, corn dollies were made for a special reason.

The fields were standing tall with wheat. It was golden and ripe and ready for cutting. When the wind blew, the fields waved and rippled like a yellow sea.

'Start cutting tomorrow,' the men said, 'Let's hope it doesn't rain before then.'

'We'll need to choose a leader,' the men said. 'We need to choose a King of the Mowers.'

They always chose a tall strong man; he had to be skilled at cutting the corn.

'We'll have Boamer as King,' they said. They'd chosen Boamer for the last few years now. They gave him red poppies and green bindweed to thread in the red ribbon round his hat. His flower-hat became his crown, and because he was tall, the men could see him clearly wherever he was in the field.

At sunrise the next day they started. They worked together as one team, up the fields and down them, cutting the stalks by hand – there were no machines in those days. Boamer gave instructions: cut here, walk there, time for a break soon. Always time for a break soon, never now.

'Set yourself more than you can do, and you'll do it,' he said.

They worked as they had never worked before; all of them, the whole village, men, women and children. It was hot work in the sun. Dry work, thirsty work, with never a time for a break.

'Keep going,' said Boamer. 'Keep up. We must get the whole of the harvest in before the weather breaks, before the rain comes, or the harvest will be spoiled.'

They worked harder still. They cut the corn, and turned it in the sun so that it would dry. They stacked the stalks and bound them with straw into sheaves. They propped the sheaves against each other to carry on drying in the sun.

Boamer said they could stop for dinner, and they all collapsed on the ground and ate bread and cheese out of baskets that their wives brought. But as soon as they had eaten they had to start work again – mowing, reaping, binding.

The sun went in and the sky grew grey.

'Work harder,' shouted Boamer, 'We must get all the harvest in before the weather breaks. Load up the carts. Get the sheaves to the stack-yard before it rains.'

They loaded the sheaves on to the horse carts and drove the carts to the yard. While some of them drove the carts back for the next load, others stacked the corn to keep it dry. Backwards and forwards went the carts, people and horses working as hard as they could.

The rain stayed away and they worked until night-time, until there was no longer any light to see by.

'Back at first light in the morning,' called Boamer. 'There's still more work to do.'

They had no sooner gone to bed and fallen asleep, than it was time to get up and start work all over again. They were exhausted. But no-one stopped, no-one gave up, everyone kept on working. A good harvest meant they would all have bread in the winter.

Towards the end of the fourth day, the last field was cut. The rain had kept off, and the corn was dry. The women went home to prepare the feast.

'Boamer,' called the men, 'Here's the last sheaf.' They all gathered quietly round the last sheaf of corn in the last field. Boamer silently picked out the strongest and straightest stalks from the sheaf. He held them in his big hands and the men stood and watched. Without saying a word, Boamer started to plait and weave the stalks together. His fingers worked quickly and well. Slowly the corn dolly took shape. He pulled out the red ribbon from his straw hat and tied the end of the corn dolly fast, and held it high in the air. The men suddenly burst into shouting and singing, laughter and dancing. The harvest was in. It was finished. And the corn dolly was made. It had to be made from the last sheaf every year. And next year it would be untied and its seeds would be the first seeds sown for the new crop. And so it went on, harvest after harvest after harvest.

Now there was one more job to do.

'Come on,' shouted Boamer.

They all ran along the lane towards the farmhouse.

'Harvest home! Harvest home!' they sang.

'The boughs do shake and the bells do ring,
Merrily comes our harvest in.
We've ploughed, we've sowed.
We've reaped, we've mowed,
We've brought our harvest in.
The boughs do shake and the bells do ring,
Merrily comes our harvest in.'

When they arrived at the farmhouse, the harvest home dinner was ready. And what a dinner it was! A feast fit for the people who had worked so hard to bring the harvest home. And sitting in pride of place in the middle of the table, was the corn dolly, to remind them of their hard work and success.

Whenever you see a corn dolly, you'll be able to think of all the hard work that used to go in to the harvest, before the days of big powerful farm machinery. Some people believe that the corn dolly is a reminder that God keeps his promise of harvest every year. Sometimes the harvest is poor because the rain comes at the wrong time, or even not at all. But there is enough harvest in the world, if we share it out amongst everyone who needs it.

Prayer
Thank you God for the harvest. Thank you for all our food, and the people who grow and prepare it. Please help us to know that there is enough food for everyone, if it is shared out fairly.

Amen

Hymn
'Look for signs that summer's done' *Someone's singing, Lord*

Practical ideas
A corn dolly is obviously needed for this assembly. They are usually easy to find in craft shops. Children can experiment with making their own corn dollies using art straws and ribbon. Older children could try making the real thing; straightforward plaits are perhaps the easiest to make. Brittle straw can be soaked in warm water to make it more pliable. Surplus straw should be wrapped in a damp cloth whilst work is in progress.

Fresh maize leaves can also be fashioned into dollies. Use cotton or wool to tie the leaves to form head and body. The head can be stuffed with a little cotton wool.

In many cultures through the centuries, the empty 'corn-cob' itself has been a children's doll. Traditionally it was dressed in its own leaves. Children may like to create their own corn-cob doll, by adding wool hair and a felt-pen face.

Biblical references to the theme   *Week 5   Responsibility*

'The whole crowd answered, "Let the responsibility for his death fall on us and our children!" '

Matthew 27:25

'Take your places in the Temple by clans, according to the responsibilities assigned to you . . . and arrange yourselves so that some of you will be available to help each family of the people of Israel.'

2 Chronicles 35:4-5

'When you build a new house, be sure to put a railing round the edge of the roof. Then you will not be responsible if someone falls off and is killed.'

Deuteronomy 22:8

A story about Nobody

The other day when I was walking through the cloakroom, I saw a coat on the floor. There were several children nearby, but when I asked whose it was, everyone said it wasn't theirs and they all carried on doing what they were doing. Then, one very sensible boy said, 'It isn't mine but I'll pick it up and then it won't get trodden on.'

That boy was showing that he was responsible. He knew that looking after things in school is everyone's job and everyone needs to help.

I know that when it's time to tidy up in the classroom, some people think they only need to tidy away their own things. But responsible people try to tidy away anything that needs it, even if they were not the last person to use something.

Everyone in our school is responsible for looking after our school. It's not just the job of the teachers or the oldest children; it's everyone's job.

Once upon a time there were four people who had very unusual names. I'd like to introduce the people to you.*

This is 'Everybody'.

Here is 'Somebody'.

This is 'Anybody'.

And last, I'd like you to meet 'Nobody'.

At the time our story begins, Everybody, Somebody, Anybody and Nobody all lived together in the same house. They all got along well together and each did their share of the work. But one day there was a *very* important job to be done, and then the trouble started.

Everybody said 'Somebody will do it'.

Now Anybody could have done it, but in the end Nobody did it.

Somebody became very angry and said 'It's Everybody's job!'

But Everybody said 'Anybody should have done it!'

Nobody knew that Everybody wouldn't do it.

In the end, Everybody blamed Somebody because Anybody could have done the very important job, but Nobody did it.

In our school, let's make sure that if there's a job to be done, we do it. Let's not leave it, in the hope that someone else will do it. If we do that, it will be like the story and in the end who will do it? Yes, Nobody.

Prayer
Dear God, help us to do a job sensibly if we see it needs doing. Help us each to take our share of the responsibility for doing the jobs in our school.

Amen

Hymn
'When I needed a neighbour' *Come and Praise* Vol 1

Practical ideas
*Because of its abstract nature, this story is difficult for young children to understand. I found the story worked best when four children were brought out to be the four characters. Each child held a card with their character's name written clearly on it. As the story progressed, the characters were identified. After the story had been told once, the child playing 'Nobody' was asked to sit down, and his name-card was attached to an empty chair. The story was then retold and the audience was able to join in by saying the character names as the story progressed. It would also be possible for four able children to enact the story for the audience.

There are several poems for young children on the theme of 'Nobody'. Perhaps the best known of these is the traditional rhyme 'Mr Nobody'. This can be found in *The book of a thousand poems* published by Collins ISBN 0 00 312526 2.

Flowers for a duchess
Week 5 *Responsibility*

Have you ever had a bad day when everything seemed to go wrong and everyone seemed to be cross with you? Sometimes if you've done something careless or silly, your mum or dad, or your teacher might say, 'Oh, you are irresponsible!' They mean you were not thinking very carefully, or that you were not thinking ahead at the time.

Today's story is about someone who was told she was irresponsible, but in the end she proved they were wrong to say that about her. It's a true story. It really happened, and not very long ago.

In a village called Clifford in Yorkshire, a new hospice for children was going to be built. The architect had drawn the plans, the builders had been chosen, but all the arranging had taken a very long time. At last, work was due to begin. The Duchess of Kent had been invited to lay the Foundation Stone – the very first stone of the brand new building.

Near to the hospice were some houses, and Nicola lived in one of them. She was seven years old and liked going to school. But, on the day this story begins, she was not having a good day!

Everyone in the house was late out of bed and everyone was hurrying to get the day started. Nicola reached across the breakfast table to get her cereal and knocked over the milk. It spread in a great white pool over the table. There was such a lot of it.

'Now look what you've done,' shouted her mum, 'You're so irresponsible. Never thinking. Always in a rush.' And she went away to get a cloth to mop up the milk.

'Never mind,' said her dad, 'No use crying over spilt milk. I know you're responsible and grown-up. Tell you what, you prove it today,' and he gave her a hug and set off for work.

Nicola decided to try to do what her dad had said. She knew she was responsible, she'd show everyone she was, and prove her mum wrong.

On the way to school, Nicola saw one of the small children fall and cut his knee. She took him in to school and helped one of the teachers to look after him.

During the morning a visitor came in to Nicola's classroom and spent a long time talking to Mrs Adams. Some of the children started to be noisy and silly, but Nicola tried to be responsible and get on with her work.

At lunch-time one of the servers was away on Nicola's table. Although children in her class weren't usually servers, Nicola was asked if she could help. She did her best and the dinner lady told Mrs Adams how sensible she had been.

At the beginning of afternoon school, Mrs Adams told the class that she was looking for a responsible person to do a very special job. She told the children about the Duchess of Kent coming to Clifford the next day to lay the foundation stone of the new hospice.

'We'll all go together to watch her drive through the village,' she said. 'Then we need six very sensible children who can represent the school at the Foundation Stone Ceremony. One of those children will be chosen to present flowers to the Duchess of Kent.'

Later that afternoon, the headteacher came in to Nicola's classroom and told her that she had been chosen as one of the six representatives of the school, and that she would be going to the ceremony the next day. 'Wear your smartest school clothes,' she said, and then she whispered something in Nicola's ear.

At hometime Nicola could hardly wait to tell her mum and dad her news.

'You see,' she said to her mum, 'I am responsible. Mrs Adams said so.'

'I know you are,' said her mum. 'I'm sorry I said you weren't.'

The next day Nicola was up very early to get ready for school. The six children who had been chosen to go to the ceremony were taken to the Martin House Hospice by car, even though it was only a short way from school. Soon the Duchess of Kent arrived and as she stepped out of her car to meet the people, Nicola walked forward, curtsied, and handed the Duchess a beautiful basket of flowers.

'Thank you,' said the Duchess of Kent, and she smiled at Nicola and asked her name and wanted to know all about her school.

Why do you think Nicola was chosen to present the flowers to the Duchess? I think it was because she had shown that she could be sensible and reliable and responsible. She certainly enjoyed meeting the Duchess of Kent and watching the Foundation Stone Ceremony. Perhaps she'll tell her children about it, when she's grown up.

Prayer

Help us, Lord, to be responsible people. Help us to be sensible. Help us to do our best all the time.

Amen

Hymn

'The wise may bring their learning'   *Come and Praise* Vol 1

The monkey and the bridge

adapted from the Mahākapi-Jātaka

Week 5   Responsibility

Who is responsible for looking after you? Yes, your parents at home, and the teachers here at school are responsible for making sure you are safe and well. Of course, you also have a responsibility to look after yourself and to be sensible. Have you ever been asked to be responsible for someone else? If you have a pet you might have been asked to be responsible for that, and it might be your job to feed it and care for it. Or perhaps you've been asked to help look after a younger brother or sister. You might have been asked to be responsible for someone younger here at school, at playtime or lunchtime. If you're responsible for someone, it's your duty to care for them. Today's story is about someone who cared for others, even more than he cared for himself.

The Bodhisatta – who was a very wise one – was once a ruler of monkeys. One day he found a fruit tree at the edge of a river. He led his troupe of monkeys to it, so that they could feed. The fruit was rich, ripe and delicious and the monkeys ate hungrily.

One of the branches of the fruit tree was growing low near the water; as the monkeys climbed in the tree, the branch bent lower and lower and dipped into the river itself. One of the fruits was pulled from the branch by the swirling of the water, and in no time it was being swept along downstream.

The fruit floated and bobbed in the river and was suddenly caught in a fisherman's net. He pulled in his net, pulled out the fruit, and looked at it.

'I've never seen anything quite like this,' he said. 'I wonder what kind of

fruit it is? Perhaps it's very rare. Perhaps the king would like it for his tea.'
So the fisherman gathered up his fishing tackle and set off for the palace, to
offer the very rare fruit to the king.

The king's taster tasted it. 'Delicious,' he said.

The king tasted it. 'Quite exquisite,' he said. 'Bring me more.'

The king's foresters were sent to follow the course of the river and find
the tree where the fruit had grown. They found it. And they found the
group of monkeys climbing in the tree, and eating all the fruit.

'Kill the monkeys,' shouted the chief forester.

The men had bows and arrows with them, and quickly surrounded the
tree. The arrows were pulled from quivers and fitted to the bows. The
archers began to take aim at the monkeys.

'What shall we do?' screamed the monkeys as they jumped down from
the tree in terror.

'Do not fear,' said the Bodhisatta. 'I will give you life.' He ran along the
low branch of the tree and jumped from the branch end to the other side of
the river. He snatched a bamboo pole and pushed the end of it in the soft
wet mud of the river bank. Then he swung across with the other end and
caught hold of the low branch of the fruit tree on the far side of the river,
where the monkeys were. He had now made a bridge, with himself as the
middle section between the low branch and the bamboo pole.

'Quick,' he called to the monkeys. 'As fast as the wind, over my back
and away.'

The monkeys ran along the branch, over his back, and down the pole to
safety on the far bank. The arrows of the foresters fell far short of the
running monkeys. They threw down their bows and arrows and took to
their feet and tried to catch the monkeys before they could reach the safe
side of the river.

As the foresters ran to the low branch, the last of the monkeys was
running across it. But this monkey did not like the Bodhisatta, and he
jumped hard on his back as he ran over.

The Bodhisatta felt such pain, he couldn't move. The foresters ran along
the low branch and grabbed him. They pulled him off the branch and pole,
regardless of the pain he was in. They held him fast and hauled him off to
see the king.

'Kill him!' they said. 'He has led that whole band of monkeys to the fruit
tree and they have stripped it bare of its fruit. He has no right to live. Kill
him!'

'It is not right to kill him,' said the King. 'He has brought safety to all the
others without a thought for his own safety. He has cared for those he rules,
more than he has cared for himself. He has much to teach us.' And the king
gently led the Bodhisatta in to his own rooms and looked after him.

The Bodhisatta could have jumped across the river and saved himself without bothering to go back and make a bridge so that everyone else could escape. But he knew he was responsible for the rest of the monkeys, and if he had not tried to save them, he would have remembered that for the rest of his life.

Prayer
Dear God, help us to be responsible when we have to care for someone else. Help us to think of their safety as well as our own when we are looking after others. Help us to be responsible with our pets, and our younger brothers and sisters, and the people younger than us in our school.

Amen

Hymn
'Cross over the road' *Come and Praise* Vol 1

Biblical references to the theme   *Week 6   Rules*

'For God will judge you in the same way as you judge others, and he will apply to you the same rules you apply to others.'

Matthew 7:2

'An athlete who runs in a race cannot win the prize unless he obeys the rules.'

2 Timothy 2:5

Fair's fair   *Week 6   Rules*
adapted from Aesop

Have you ever tried to play a game where one of the other people doesn't know the rules? It's not possible to get very far in the game, is it? Everyone who's playing needs to know what they are allowed to do, and what they're not allowed to do.

And have you ever been in the middle of a game when someone has tried to change the rules, usually so that they can win? That's the same as cheating, isn't it?

Once the rules are decided, the players have to abide by them, or the whole game becomes unfair. In today's story, the people were not playing a game, but nevertheless someone tried to change the rules.

Once upon a time an old woman went blind. She was very upset and sent for her doctor. She promised the doctor she would give him a large reward if only he could make her well again, and able to see.

'But if you are not able to make me see again,' she said, 'I shall pay you nothing.'

The doctor agreed that this was fair, and they both signed an official contract to say that they agreed to the arrangement. Then they shook hands on it.

The doctor examined the old lady, and soon discovered what was wrong with her. Luckily it wasn't a very serious illness and he knew that he could make her well again quite easily and quickly. But he decided not to. He decided to let her think his treatment would take a long time. He decided that if he did this, she would think he was very clever and then she would pay him a bigger reward.

The doctor visited the old woman every day and pretended to treat her with ointments and creams. Each day whilst he waited for the pretend medicines to work, he noticed the valuable things that the old woman had in her home. The doctor decided to steal some of her things while she was still blind. 'She won't see they're missing,' he said.

So each day, when he visited, he stole something that belonged to her. He took a picture and then a brooch. He stole an ornament and a golden box and small lamp. Then he became really greedy and took a small table and an antique chair. Then he stole a bookcase, and finally he hired a furniture removal van and stole her grand piano and the settee.

By now there was nothing left that the doctor wanted, so he gave the old lady the medicine he should have given her in the first place, and after two days she was able to see again.

'But where are my things?' she asked, when she could see. 'I used to have lots of lovely things. You must have stolen them. No-one else has been here. You stole my things.' And she refused to pay him the reward she had promised for making her see again.

'You have to pay me,' the doctor said. 'You promised. We agreed. We signed a contract. We shook hands on it. You have to pay me my reward.'

'No!' said the old lady. 'Not until you bring me back my things.'

'Yes!' said the doctor. 'You agreed.'

'No!' she said.

'Yes!' he said.

'No!'

'Yes!'

'No!'

In the end they both had to go to court to let a judge decide whether or not the doctor should have the money that the old woman had promised he could have, if he made her able to see again.

The doctor explained his side of the story.

The old woman explained hers.

'And did you promise to pay him?' said the judge.

'Yes,' said the old woman. 'I promised to pay him a reward if he cured me. But he hasn't cured me.'

'That's a lie,' shouted the doctor. 'Of course I cured her. She can see, can't she?'

'No I can't,' she said. 'Before I went blind I could see all the beautiful things in my home. I could see my pictures and my ornaments, my jewellery and my lovely grand piano. Then I went blind and I couldn't see any of those things. Then the doctor came and said he cured me, but I still can't see any of my things. So, it's quite clear; he hasn't cured me. Therefore he doesn't get paid.'

The judge ruled that the old woman was right, and the doctor was sent away without getting his reward.

I wonder if you think that was fair. I wonder what *you* would have decided, if *you* had been the judge. I hope that if you agree to something, you'll keep your word. That's why it's important to think carefully before you agree to anything.

Prayer

Dear God, please help us to keep our word when we have agreed to something. Help us to play games fairly, and not try to cheat or change the rules part way through.

Amen

Hymn

'The ink is black, the page is white' *Come and Praise* Vol 1

Three bears   *Week 6   Rules*

Some of the rules we have at our school and in the world, are there to help people be safe. Can you think of any rules like this? Yes, we have rules about not playing with fire and we have road safety rules called the Green Cross Code and the Highway Code. We have the Countryside Code which tells us what to do so that we don't harm farm animals or wild animals. In our school we have rules telling us not to run indoors and not to play rough games in the playground.

All those rules are to help us keep ourselves and our environment safe.

But sometimes people forget the rules. In today's story, someone forgot the rule about rough play.

Once upon a time there were three bears. Their names were Tiny Bear, Helpful Bear and Bully Bear. They all went to school together and they all played together every playtime. And every playtime was the same; Bully Bear bullied Tiny Bear, then Helpful Bear tried to help.

Helpful noticed that it was always Tiny Bear, or other little bears, that Bully Bear upset. She never bullied the bigger bears. She never took their honey sandwiches or spoiled their games. She never hid their toys or pushed them in the mud.

One day Helpful Bear was comforting Tiny Bear because Bully Bear had pushed him over and hurt him. Helpful Bear said 'There, There, you'll soon feel better.' He gave Tiny Bear a cuddle and shared his honey lollipop with him. Then he thought, 'It's all very well helping Tiny Bear every time he gets upset, but it's really Bully Bear that needs sorting out. I'm going to find her next playtime.'

At first, Helpful Bear couldn't see her. Then he spotted Bully Bear standing by herself, kicking stones at nowhere in particular. Now you might be thinking that Helpful Bear was going to give Bully Bear a taste of her own medicine. But you'd be wrong! Helpful Bear knew that two wrongs don't make a right. He knew that if he started to fight Bully Bear than he would be just as wrong as Bully had been. No! Helpful Bear didn't go and pick a fight. He went up to Bully Bear and said

'Hello. Do you want to play?'

'No. Nobody plays with me,' said Bully Bear. 'They don't want to.'

'Why not?' asked Helpful Bear.

'Because I'm not nice,' said Bully Bear.

'Well, perhaps if you tried to be nice,' said Helpful Bear, 'people would want to be nice to you, then you'd want to be nice to them, then they'd want to be nice to you back; if you see what I mean.'

Bully Bear thought.

But she didn't answer.

'Well, please yourself,' said Helpful Bear. 'But it's surely better than standing here on your own. Anyway, I'm going to play with Tiny Bear. Do you want to come, or not?'

'I don't think he'll want to play with me,' said Bully Bear.

'He will if you say you're sorry,' said Helpful Bear. 'Come on.'

So Bully Bear went across the playground with Helpful Bear, and they found Tiny Bear. Bully Bear muttered some sort of apology about playing roughly, and Tiny Bear said all right, although he was very scared of Bully Bear coming to play with them and he didn't think it was a good idea.

Helpful Bear suggested that they play hide and seek. The other two agreed, and they played. Bully Bear thought it was a bit tame at first. There was no rough and tumble and she couldn't hit or kick or fight. But soon she found she was enjoying playing the game. They played properly and kept to the rules. They had fair turns at hiding and seeking and some more bears came along and joined in.

Later, at the next playtime, they all played again, but this time it was a different game. Bully Bear was so busy playing with her new friends, she forgot all about bullying.

A few weeks later it was Helpful Bear's birthday. He had a party and invited all his friends. They all brought him birthday presents – honey cakes, honey buns, honey sweets, and sticky-honey-toffee-apples. But the best birthday present of all came from Bully Bear.

'Here's my biggest jar of runny honey,' she said. 'It's for you. To say Happy Birthday. And to say thank you for helping me to be a nice bear and showing me how to make friends. It's better being friends than being a bully.'

'You'll need a new name,' said Helpful Bear. 'We can't call you Bully Bear now. What name will you choose?'

I wonder what Bully Bear decided to call herself. Perhaps she chose Brave Bear or Buddy Bear. What would you have chosen?

Sometimes, we need to be like Helpful Bear, and help people remember the rules.

Prayer
Dear God, please help us to remember the rules that are there to keep us safe. Help us to remind our friends if they forget the rules. Help us to remember not to hurt or frighten anyone.

Amen

Hymn
'Think, think on these things' *Someone's singing, Lord*

The bee who wanted to be different   *Week 6   Rules*

Do you like to be the same as everyone else, or do you like to be different – to stand out from the crowd, and be individual? Some people like to be the same as other people and some people like to be different. And that's right, because everyone has their own ideas about these things. But, whether people like to be the same, or like to be different, people must fit in and follow rules when they live together in a community.

In our school, we like you all to think for yourselves, but we need you all to work together, because there are a lot of us in our building. If we all went around doing just what we want to do, whenever we want to do it, our school would be a dreadful place.

In today's story, a bee decided she wanted to be different from everyone else.

They were having their first lesson in cell building. All the young bees were being taught how to make beeswax. Then they were shown how to make the wax into honeycombs. These honeycombs were made of lots and lots of little six-sided shapes which all fitted together perfectly. Some of the six-sided cells would be for the queen bee to lay eggs in, and some of the six-sided cells would become the storage cells for the golden honey when it was made.

One bee wanted to be different.

'I don't see why I have to be the same as everyone else,' she said. 'I don't want to make beeswax cells that shape. I don't see why they have to have six sides. Six is a silly number.' And she began to make beeswax cells that were a different size and shape from everyone else's.

'You can't do that,' said the other bees, when they saw what she was doing.

'Oh yes I can,' she said. 'You watch me,' and she made another cell with three short sides and two long ones.

'Take that cell out and make a hexagon,' said the teacher-bee voice behind her.

'See, we knew you'd get into trouble,' giggled the others.

The bee who wanted to be different watched as the teacher moved away to look at another bee's cells.

'I won't do it that way,' she said. 'I'll do it my own way. I won't do it the same as them.' And she carried on making curiously shaped cells with any number of sides except six.

At the end of the morning the teacher asked each bee to fit the cells she had made to the cells made by the other bees. They all began to do as they were told. Soon the whole honeycomb fitted together beautifully; all except for the part made by the bee who wanted to be different. That part didn't fit in at all. It had corners and angles that stuck out in all directions. None of its sides matched the sides of the other cells.

'I'm sorry,' said the teacher bee. 'But you can't share with our honeycomb. If you want to be different and make a comb of your own, you'll have to go and live somewhere else.'

The bee who wanted to be different looked at the teacher bee. She thought she was joking. But then, to her horror, she realised that the teacher bee meant she had to leave.

'But where will I live?' she said. 'This bee-hive is my home. I don't know anywhere else. Please let me stay.'

'I'm sorry,' said the teacher bee, 'but honey bees live together as a community. They work together. They fit in with the rest of the hive. If a bee wants to be different, and do things in a different way, she must go and live alone in a hollow tree or a crack in a rock. Do you still want to be different?'

'Yes!' shouted the bee who wanted to be different. The truth of the matter was that she no longer wanted to be different at all, but she was being defiant and difficult.

'Yes!' she shouted again. 'I want to be different.'

'Then out you go,' said the teacher bee, and she chased her out of the hive and over the field, across the moor and beyond.

It wasn't a very happy ending for the bee who wanted to be different, was it? When people or creatures live together in a community, they have to fit in with the community, if it is to work well.

Prayer
Help us Lord, to know that we need to work together, and not against each other, in our school. Help us to work together and play together and make our school a good community to belong to.

Amen

Hymn
'Hey, now, everybody sing' *Alleluya*

Practical ideas
I linked this assembly to the manufacture of a hand-made patchwork quilt. Bees, and some patchworkers, use hexagons. Bees, and patchworkers, need to conform in making standard shapes so that the pieces will connect together correctly. If you don't have access to a patchwork quilt to show the children, a drawing of tesselated hexagons can be shown. Or, children can be asked to 'be' the bees and draw the hexagonal shapes on paper, using templates. One child can be the bee who wanted to be different, and produce irregular shapes. The 'work' can then be cut out and fitted together at the appropriate time in the story.

Biblical references to the theme   Week 7   Caring

'Take care of a fig tree and you will have figs to eat.'

Proverbs 27:18

'A good man takes care of his animals, but wicked men are cruel to theirs.'

Proverbs 12:10

'So keep watch over yourselves and over all the flock which the Holy Spirit has placed in your care.'

Acts 20:28

The cormorant   Week 7   Caring

One of the things I like to do in my spare time is to go swimming, and I know many of you like swimming too. Not long ago, when I was on holiday in Majorca, I went swimming in the sea every morning, and nearly every morning I had a companion in the water with me. But it wasn't a person . . . it was a cormorant.

The first time I saw the cormorant I could hardly believe what I was seeing. It was standing on a rock, only a very short distance from where I was swimming. I stayed as still as I could and floated just a little nearer to the rock. The cormorant stood still and watched me, and I watched the cormorant.

It was beautiful. It had sleek dark shiny feathers and a long body with a pale-coloured front. It had black shiny beady eyes and big webbed feet. It had a long beak with a little hook on the end. I had never been so near a cormorant before, and I felt very lucky to be so close to it without it flying away.

Suddenly, it plopped in to the water and started to swim; not away, but backwards and forwards in the same patch of water I was in. And how it could swim! It could dive without making even a tiny splash; it could dart really quickly under the water; it could twist and turn so fast I could hardly watch it; and it could catch fish. There were lots of small silvery-coloured fish in the water, and every so often the cormorant would dive straight towards one. It never missed.

After about five minutes of swimming near me, the cormorant climbed out of the sea on to a rock and stood with its wings stretched out, as if it were hanging them out to dry.

Early every morning when I went down to the sea for a swim, the cormorant was in the water fishing for its breakfast. Sometimes there might be someone else swimming as well, but there were never more than one or two people. Later in the day when lots of people came to swim, the cormorant would stand on the rocks and watch. It didn't seem to be afraid of people, and the people were very careful not to frighten or startle the cormorant. People moved about quietly and gently when they were near it. Lots of people took photographs of it. But no-one did anything which might hurt it.

The cormorant gave a great many people a lot of pleasure just by being there. I liked watching the new holiday-makers, and the look of surprise on their faces when they saw the cormorant for the first time.

On the last day of my holiday, when I had packed my case and was almost ready to leave for the airport, I decided to take one last walk down to the sea, and say goodbye to the cormorant, if it was there.

When I arrived at the rocks where the cormorant usually sat, I saw a small crowd of people. They were all talking quietly and one lady was crying. It seemed that the cormorant was hurt. It had a large cut on the side of its head and it couldn't walk or swim properly.

'What happened?' I said.

'A boy has been throwing stones at it,' said a man. 'I tried to stop him but I was too late. I don't think the cormorant will live.'

That boy had hurt a beautiful creature, and had spoiled the pleasure of lots of people on holiday. Everyone else had respected the cormorant and had done their best not to frighten it or hurt it. In return, the cormorant had trusted the people. And then a boy, in one silly moment, had destroyed that trust.

I don't know whether the cormorant survived. I hope it did. But I know how angry I felt about that boy's cruelty, and I know I shall never forget how much I enjoyed swimming with the cormorant.

Prayer

Dear God, help us to respect all living things. Help us to care for them and to do nothing to hurt them. Help us to care for all creatures and to care for our world.

Amen

Hymn

'From the tiny ant' *Come and Praise* Vol 2

Practical ideas

Many children will have little idea of what a cormorant looks like. This assembly inspired a display of bird books which in turn inspired some children to do further research on sea birds. The following books have good illustrations and facts about cormorants:

Birds of Britain published by the Readers' Digest, 1981;
Birdwatch by Tony Soper published by Webb & Bower, 1982;
A field guide in colour to birds by Dr Walter Cerny published by Octopus Books, 1983.

Three things   *Week 7   Caring*

I wonder how carefully you look after your toys and books and clothes at home. I know that at school some of you are very good at looking after your things; and some of you are not-so-good at looking after your books and belongings! Today's story is about a man who was asked to take care of his neighbour's things for a while.

There was once a man called Ahmed who owned a wooden chair, a china plate and a little wooden box. These three things were very precious to him, but no-one knew why. It was clear that the three things mattered to him because of the careful way he looked after them. The chair was always beautifully polished, the plate was always sparklingly clean, and the little wooden box was dusted every day and had a lovely gleaming shine to it.

One winter Ahmed had to go on a journey. He knew he would be away from home for quite some time, so he asked Hussein, his neighbour, to look after the chair, the plate and the little wooden box.

'Of course I'll look after them for you,' said Hussein. 'I'll look after them as if they were my own.'

'Thank you,' said Ahmed, and he took the three things round to Hussein's house, then set off on his journey.

Hussein looked at the three things and wondered why Ahmed was so concerned about them. They looked very ordinary things. They didn't look at all special or remarkable or valuable.

Hussein sat on the wooden chair.

'It's quite a comfortable chair,' he said. 'I think I'll put it by the kitchen fire and use it every day. Ahmed won't mind.'

Then Hussein looked at the plate. It was a white plate, patterned with blue and yellow daisies.

'It's quite a pretty plate,' he said. 'I think I'll put it on the table and use it every day. Ahmed won't mind.'

Hussein then picked up the little wooden box. He turned it over and round in his hands; the wood felt warm and smooth. He tried to open the box, but he couldn't work out how to do it, it didn't seem to have a fastener or any hinges. In the end Hussein decided it didn't open at all, and he threw it into the back of a drawer.

Over the next few weeks, Hussein used the chair every day, but he never polished it. Soon the chair looked dull and shabby. The back of it became faded with sunlight and the front of it became scorched with sparks from the fire.

Hussein used the plate every day as well. One day he dropped it and a long crack appeared across the middle of the daisies. Another day he baked a pie for a friend and gave it to him on the daisy plate. When the plate came back again, it was chipped in two places.

Hussein forgot all about the little wooden box.

At the end of the winter Ahmed came back.

'I've come for my things,' he said.

When Hussein showed him the chair and the plate he was very upset.

'That chair was very special to me,' he said. 'It was made for me by a blind man when he was very old. He made it with love and care and I promised I would look after it with love and care.'

'I'm sorry,' said Hussein.

'And that plate belonged to my great-grandmother. It's the only thing I have of hers.'

'I'm sorry,' said Hussein.

'And the little wooden box holds a secret. Where is the little wooden box?'

'I don't know,' said Hussein. 'Yes I do. I put it in a drawer.' Hussein remembered he had thrown the box in the drawer when he couldn't find a way to open it. He rummaged about in the drawer and searched everywhere for it, but he couldn't find it.

'I'm sorry,' he said. 'I've lost it.'

'It had a secret lock,' said Ahmed. 'Only I could open it, so I knew the diamonds were safe.'

'Diamonds?' said Hussein.

'Yes,' said Ahmed. 'I had some diamonds in the box. I was going to give you one when I got home.'

'I'm sorry,' said Hussein again. 'I've not taken good care of your things.'

'Never mind,' said Ahmed. 'I forgive you. We're still friends.' And they shook hands on it.

I don't know whether the little wooden box ever turned up, but I do know that Ahmed was very kind to forgive Hussein. I think I would have felt very angry if someone hadn't looked after my things. I hope you look after things that belong to other people better than Hussein did.

Prayer
Thank you God, for things that are special to us. Help us to take care of our things at home and at school. Help us to look after other people's things as well as our own.

Amen

Hymn
'When your Father made the world'   *Come and Praise* Vol 2

Mrs Edwards and the sewing machine   *Week 7   Caring*

This week in assembly we've been thinking about caring: caring for animals and caring for things. I hope all the people in our school will do their best all the time, to care for everyone and everything around them, and to care for our school and our neighbourhood as well. But there's someone else I hope you'll care for; I hope you'll care for *you*, and look after *yourself*. Today's story is about someone who expected everyone else to look after her. She didn't think it was her job to be responsible for herself.

Mrs Edwards had two children, and when they were both old enough to go to school, she decided she'd like to get a job. She looked in the newspaper to see what jobs were available, and saw a small advertisement which said
'Wanted. Machinist – to sew children's clothes.
Apply to the manager at Barton's factory.'
'That's exactly the right job for me,' she siad. 'I'll apply for it.'
So she went along to the factory to see the manager and to ask for a job.
'I can use a sewing machine,' she said. 'And I know how to make children's clothes. I make them for my own children.'
'You can start on Monday,' said the manager, and he showed her the sewing machine and the room where she would be working. There were lots of other people in the room, all working away at their sewing machines. At the end of the room was a table with neat piles of finished clothes on it.
'I'm looking forward to coming,' said Mrs Edwards.
The next Monday she arrived at the factory bright and early and started work at her sewing machine. She noticed that this machine was different from hers at home. This one had a small plastic guard in front of the needle to stop her getting her fingers caught. But Mrs Edwards didn't like the

guard, it seemed to get in the way, so she took it off the sewing machine, and carried on her work without it.

Mrs Edwards worked quickly and well. By lunchtime she had a lot of finished clothes stacked up on her sewing table. She also had an enormous scattering of bits of cloth and thread, on the floor all around her. She knew she was supposed to tidy up at lunchtime, but she thought that if she left it, someone else would probably do it for her.

After lunch, she sat at her machine and started work again. But she'd only been sewing for a couple of minutes when somehow she tangled her fingers in the cloth, and before she knew what was happening, the needle had stitched into her thumb.

'Ow,' she shouted. She carefully pulled her hand away from the sewing machine and stood up to go and get a plaster. But, as she walked away from her place, she slipped on the scattered pieces of cloth on the floor, and twisted her ankle as she fell.

The manager came hurrying over to see what was the matter.

'I'm hurt,' shouted Mrs Edwards. 'And it's all your fault. You shouldn't allow your workers to have accidents. You should look after people better than this. That machine has stitched into my thumb and now I've fallen on all this rubbish. It's all your fault.'

'I don't think it's the fault of the factory, Mrs Edwards,' said the manager.

'Oh yes it is. I'm going to take you to court about this,' And Mrs Edwards struggled to her feet and limped away home.

A few weeks later Mrs Edwards and the factory manager had to appear before a judge at a meeting to decide whose fault the accident really was. Mrs Edwards was sure she was not to blame. She was therefore very surprised indeed when the judge said

'I'm sorry, Mrs Edwards, but you cannot blame the factory or the manager. There was a guard on that machine which you took off, and you did not tidy up at lunchtime when you were supposed to. Yes, the factory has a responsibility to look after you, but you also have a responsibility to look after yourself. On that Monday you did not look after yourself. The fault, Mrs Edwards, was yours.'

Everyone everywhere has a responsibility to try to look after themselves and keep themselves safe.

On Bonfire Night lots of people are responsible for keeping children and adults safe. The people who make fireworks must make them safely so that they don't go off at the wrong time. The people who organise firework shows and bonfire parties must make safe arrangements. And if you go to a bonfire party, or have fireworks to watch, *you* are responsible for keeping *yourself* safe, by being sensible and by following the firework code.

Prayer
Dear God, help us to know that we each have a responsibility to try to keep ourselves safe, and to look after ourselves. Help us to think ahead and to behave sensibly, so that we don't cause accidents. Please help everyone to be safe on Bonfire Night.

Amen

Hymn
'God in his love'   *Come and Praise* Vol 2

Practical ideas
During the week of Bonfire Night, our school displays Firework Code Posters and other firework safety material. These are shown in assembly and followed up by appropriate classroom discussion, determined by the children's ages and local bonfire events.

The Firework Code Posters are distributed by the Consumer Safety Unit of the Department of Trade and Industry, to all schools in England, Scotland and Wales. The posters are designed for the Firework Masters' Guild, and the Code was agreed by the Guild, the Home office, RoSPA, the NSPCC and the RSPCA.

Further free safety material can be obtained from The Consumer Safety Unit, Room 406, Department of Trade and Industry, 10-18 Victoria Street, London SW1H ONN; and The Firework Makers' Guild, PO Box 29, Hove, East Sussex, BN3 5RP.

RoSPA firework safety posters and leaflets can be purchased from Home Safety Division, RoSPA, Cannon House, The Priory, Queensway, Birmingham B4 6BS.

Biblical references to the theme   *Week 8   Treasure*

'How happy I am because of your promises –
as happy as someone who finds rich treasure.'

Psalms 119:162

'Look for it (wisdom) as hard as you would for silver or some hidden treasure.'

Proverbs 2:4

'A good person brings good out of the treasure of good things in his heart;'
Luke 6:45

'In this way they store up for themselves a treasure which will be a solid foundation for the future.'
1 Timothy 6:19

The best gold   *Week 8   Treasure*

I wonder what you think of when someone says the word 'treasure'? You probably think of silver and gold, or diamonds and precious stones. Or perhaps you think of the crown jewels in the Tower of London. But treasure doesn't always mean precious things worth a lot of money. Treasure can be different things to different people, and treasure can in fact be worth nothing at all.

I've brought you some of my treasures to see. They are all worth a great deal to me, but they're not worth anything to anyone else. They wouldn't be worth any money if I tried to sell them. Today's story is about a man who found some treasure, but he didn't recognise it.

Once upon a time a man was walking in a part of the hills where he had never been before. The countryside was beautiful, the air was clear and the grass was springy and soft under his feet. There were a great many wild flowers dotted about in the grass. The man knew the names of most of them, but he kept noticing a small bright yellow flower with a head like a golden rosette. Some of the flowers had lost their petals and they had fluffy heads like pompoms.

The man bent to pick one of the white pompoms, but as soon as he touched the stem, the fluffy top disintegrated into a hundred tiny parachutes which all blew away on the wind. The man picked a golden yellow flower instead.

No sooner had the flower been picked from the ground, than the man heard a voice saying, 'This is the best gold!' The man looked around him to see where the voice came from, but he could see no-one. The voice came again: 'This is the best gold, but there's more in the rock over there.'

The man had no idea where the voice was coming from, or indeed what it meant. But he looked around again and sure enough noticed a large rock next to the footpath.

The voice spoke again. 'Tap this gold against the rock. It will open and you will find more gold inside. Help yourself, but don't forget the best gold.'

The man waited to see and hear what would happen next, but nothing did, so he went over to the rock by the side of the footpath and tapped against it with the golden yellow flower.

Suddenly there was a grating squeaking rasping grinding sound, and the huge rock split from top to bottom and revealed a black triangular gap. The man leaned forward and peered into the darkness. He could see nothing. He went inside.

At first he continued to see nothing at all, then as his eyes became used to the gloom, he saw a pile of something glistening in a corner. Gold. He dropped the flower and ran to the heap. He gathered up handfuls of shining gold coins and let them run through his fingers. They sparkled and jangled back on the mound with the others.

The man let out a whoop of joy and began cramming the gold pieces into every part of his clothing that would carry them: his pockets, his shoes, his socks, his shirt, everywhere. Then, when he could not hold another coin he climbed outside again, into the bright sunshine, and ran home as fast as his bulging clothing would allow.

When he arrived at his house, he hurled himself inside and called for his family to come and look. He began to empty his pockets and shoes and socks and shirt as fast as he could, at the same time as tell everyone what had happened out on the hills.

'And the voice said "Don't forget the best gold," and I went inside, and it opened and a big black cave appeared and I went inside and just look what . . .'

The man, his wife and their children looked at what he was turning out of his pockets and shoes and socks and shirt. Dust. A huge pile of dust in the middle of the kitchen table.

'I don't understand,' said the man, 'I saw the gold for myself. It was there. The voice said to me "Don't forget the . . ." Oh!' And he realised at once what he had done. He had forgotten the best gold. He thought the best gold had been the golden coins, but he had failed to see that sometimes the most beautiful things are free, like the golden yellow flower that he had left behind on the floor of the cave.

The man and his wife and their children went back straight away to the part of the hills where he had never seen the flower. But try as they might, they never ever again managed to open the magic cave with the piles of golden coins inside.

Do you know what the flower was that the man found? I don't think the story is telling us that a dandelion is really more precious than golden coins, but it is telling us that there is a lot of beauty in this world that is absolutely free. And that things can be precious without having to be worth a lot of money, like the things I brought to show you that are precious to me.

Prayer

Thank you God, for things that are precious to us. Help us to look after our belongings and those of other people. Help us not to be greedy.

Amen

Hymn

'The best gift' *Come and Praise* Vol 1

Practical ideas

This assembly needs a small collection of objects that are personal treasures. It is important that the objects are not of monetary value, but precious because of their age or perhaps their association with other people. I asked several members of staff to lend a 'treasure' for the assembly. The children were interested to hear whose each treasure was, and why it was of value to them.

Cornelia's treasure

Week 8   Treasure

Everyone has a special person in their life. I wonder who is the most special person to you. Perhaps it's your mum or your dad, or your grandma or your best friend. Special people mean a lot to us. They're worth more than all the treasure in the world.

Today's story is about a rich lady who lived in Roman times. Perhaps when you've listened to the story, you can decide why she was rich.

Cornelia had everything. She must have been one of the luckiest people in the whole of Rome. She had a lovely house, a kind husband, three beautiful children, lots of lovely clothes, jewels, ornaments, money. She had everything anyone could possibly want. She also had a brain, and could think and plan and work things out for herself.

Then, one day, Cornelia was given some sad news. Her husband had been killed in an accident. Cornelia was so unhappy, she didn't at first know what to do. All her friends tried to help.

'You must come and stay with us,' said one of her friends.

'You must travel,' said someone else, 'Then you will forget your unhappiness.'

'You must build a new life for yourself,' they all said.

But Cornelia said, 'I cannot think only of myself, I have my children to think of as well. I cannot leave them behind whilst I go travelling or whilst I stay with friends. My children need me.'

'Then you must find yourself a new husband,' her friends said. 'A new husband will take care of you and your children. A new husband is what you need.'

'A new husband is not what I need,' said Cornelia. 'Time to think is what I need.'

And Cornelia took time to think. Her friends tried to make her do what *they* thought was best for her. But Cornelia did her own thinking and decided for herself what *she* thought was best. She decided to speak to her children, Tiberius, Gaius and Sempronia.

'Your father was a rich man,' she told them. 'When he was alive he gave you everything you wanted, so there was no need for you to do anything for yourselves. However, he is no longer here, and now I think it best that you each work hard at your lessons, so that you become skilled and clever, and then you will not have to rely on anyone else, you will each be able to give *yourself* anything you want. What do you think?'

Her children thought, and talked amongst themselves, then Tiberius spoke for all three of them.

'We think you have given us very wise advice,' he said. 'We think we would like you to help us with our lessons. We will do our best and work hard. If we learn all that you can teach us, we will learn a great deal.'

So work began. Every day Cornelia set lessons for her three children. Every day Tiberius, Gaius and Sempronia worked hard at maths and science, history and geography. They read books and studied art and music. They painted pictures and acted plays. They had fun learning together, and every day the children became more clever and skilful.

While Cornelia and the children were working on their lessons, some of the people who had been her friends began to feel jealous.

'She's too clever for her own good,' they said.

'It's silly teaching those children,' they said.

'What does she expect will come of it? they said.

'She's got too much money,' they said.

'She wouldn't be rich though, if it wasn't for her husband who died,' they said.

'She doesn't deserve to be rich,' they said.

'We ought to have some of her money,' they said.

'Yes,' they said. 'We ought to have lots of her money.'

So the people who had been Cornelia's friends plotted against her, to get her money and wealth and riches away from her.

'She has jewels and ornaments and treasures,' said someone. 'We could take those away from her. Let's pretend there is a new law which says she must show all her treasures to us.'

'That's a good idea,' said someone else. 'Let's do it now.'

And so the people who used to be her friends, went to Cornelia's house to trick her into believing that a new law had just been passed, which said she must show them her treasures. The people were quite sure that their trick would work. They knocked on the door. Cornelia came to answer it.

'It's the new law,' they said. 'Didn't you know about it? You have to show us all your best treasures. We have to see what you have. It may be that you have too many. Go and get them.'

Cornelia disappeared inside her house. A moment later she was back.

'Here they are,' she said. 'These are my treasures. They are the most precious things in the world. They are worth more than any amount of gold.' And she showed the people who used to be her friends her three children, Tiberius, Gaius and Sempronia.

The people went away, back to their own houses. They knew that Cornelia was right; that special people are worth more than treasures. And they knew that Cornelia was too clever to be tricked by silly, greedy people.

Do you think Cornelia was rich because she had lots of money, or because she had three children she loved very much? I think special people are more valuable than lots of money.

Prayer
Thank you God for the special people in our lives. Please help us to look after our special people and be loyal to them. Help us never to let people down.

Amen

Hymn
'Happiness is' *Alleluya*

The strawberry-coloured cow　　　　　　　*Week 8 Treasure*

This week, in our assemblies, we've discovered that treasures can be different things to different people. Sometimes when someone has something special, they want more, and sometimes they can seem greedy. The person in today's story wanted something more, but it didn't turn out quite as she expected.

Many years ago and many miles away, an old woman lived in an old house on a hill. The house was tumbledown, with slates missing from the roof, glass missing from the windows and wood missing from the door. The old woman lived all alone and was, as you might have guessed, very poor. But she was also very neat and tidy, and her house, shabby though it was, was spotlessly clean. Every day the old woman had a line of billowing snowy white washing drying in the garden.

The only companion the old woman had was her goat. It was bright white and always looked as though it had been newly scrubbed with soap and water. In days gone by, the old woman and her husband had owned many animals – cows, sheep, pigs, hens, a dog and even a horse – but now the goat was the only one left.

One day the old woman, whose name no-one knew, was pegging out her washing when she glanced across the field and saw two travellers coming her way.

'Visitors!' she said. 'My! It's a good long while since I've had visitors!' She went inside her house to put the kettle on, then went outside again to greet the men.

'May we sit here on your doorstep and have a drink?' said one of the travellers.

'I've just put the kettle on for a pot of tea,' she said. 'So sit down and make yourselves at home.'

Soon the tea was made and the two travellers and the old woman began to talk.

'So, you've only the goat left now, out of all your animals?' said one of the men.

'Yes, that's all, but it gives me milk,' said the woman.

'I suppose you were better off when you had your cows and pigs and sheep and hens?' said the other man.

'Yes, I suppose I was,' answered the woman.

'What if you had a cow now?' asked the first man.

'Oh, if I had a cow now!' said the old woman. 'Well I should be rich indeed. What a treasure a cow would be to me. With a cow I should have milk to drink and milk to spare. With milk to spare I could make butter for my bread, and butter to sell at market. With butter to sell I could buy all the things I need. Glass for my windows and wood for my door. Slates for my roof and perhaps . . . a treat to eat.'

'Lend me your stick,' said the first man.

The old woman looked puzzled, but she handed her walking stick to the man. He thumped it on the ground by her doorway, just once, but just once was enough. There, large as life, appeared a fine fat cow, the colour of the ripest strawberry.

'Well! My goodness me!' said the old woman.

The travellers smiled, gave her back her stick, stood up, and said goodbye. They walked away down the hill, back the way they had come, leaving the old woman standing astonished.

After a few minutes, when she had stopped being quite so surprised, she began to think.

'A cow again. I never thought I'd see the day. Not now. Just think. A cow. Such luck. A cow will make me happy. A cow will make me rich. But . . . two cows would make me happier. Two cows would make me richer. If I had two cows I would have more milk and more butter; more butter would give me more butter-money and perhaps enough to hide away for a rainy day. It didn't look difficult. Just a thump with the stick.'

She took her walking stick in her hand and gave it a mighty thump on the ground. Sure enough, the magic worked again. An animal even bigger than before appeared before her eyes.

But this animal was no strawberry-coloured cow. This animal was the biggest, most angry, most fierce wolf she had ever seen. In no time it had gobbled the strawberry coloured cow and had run away across the hill.

The old woman looked around her. Everything was just as it had been before. The white washing billowed on the line and the bright white goat ate grass.

'Perhaps I dreamed a dream,' said the old woman. But no, there were the two travellers walking away down the hill, away from her tumbledown house.

With great difficulty the old woman ran after them.

'My cow,' she said. 'It's gone. My beautiful strawberry-coloured cow. It's been eaten by a wild and wicked wolf. Please help me to get it back again.'

'Ah!' said the travellers. 'But what did you do to make the greedy wolf come to your door?'

The old woman hung her head in shame and confessed that she had been greedy enough to want two cows instead of the one that the travellers had given her.

'You brought the greedy wolf yourself,' said a traveller. 'He came because you sent for him. Go home again.'

The woman walked slowly back up the hill to her tumbledown house.

'I'm a foolish old woman,' she said to herself. 'In future I shall know that enough is enough. I'll not be greedy again.' She didn't see the travellers smile to themselves, and she didn't see a fat, strawberry-coloured shape following her up the hill.

At least, not at first.

The old woman nearly lost her treasure by being greedy. I'm glad the travellers decided to give her the cow back again, even though she was greedy. Perhaps they did that because she wasn't usually a greedy sort of person.

Prayer
Thank you God, for presents and surprises that we are sometimes given.
Please help us not to be greedy.

Amen

Hymn
'Thank you, Lord'   *Come and Praise* Vol 1

Biblical references to the theme

Week 9   Advent

'A child is born to us!
A son is given to us!
And he will be our ruler.
He will be called, "Wonderful Counsellor,"
"Mighty God," "Eternal Father,"
"Prince of Peace." '

Isaiah 9:6

St Catherine's Day* (November 25th)

Week 9   Advent

*St Catherine's Day does not fall in Advent proper, but since it comes between 'Stir-up Sunday' and Advent, it is appropriate to include it here. It could, alternatively, be used on November 5th, with an added emphasis on firework safety.

Did you watch a firework display a few weeks ago, when it was Bonfire Night? If you did, you probably saw a Catherine Wheel. It's a circular firework that whizzes round and sprays out coloured sparks in curved patterns. Catherine Wheels are named after Saint Catherine, and it's her special day on November 25th, just a month before Christmas.

Catherine of Alexandria was the cleverest girl in Egypt, where she lived nearly 1600 years ago. Catherine was a Christian, at a time when many people did not know about Jesus.

One day, the Emperor Maxentius ordered lots of poor people to be killed. He wanted to kill them in honour of his own God, but when Catherine heard what he wanted to do, she went straight away to his palace to tell him that it was wrong and cruel to kill innocent people.

Emperor Maxentius was angry that a young girl dared to question his rule, and for a long time they argued about whether he should kill people or not. The Emperor Maxentius brought 50 of his wise men to argue on his behalf. But Catherine was so clever and so quick-thinking that she won all the arguments. She told the men about the work of Jesus, and many of the people listening became Christians when they heard what she had to say.

Emperor Maxentius became more and more angry and eventually shouted, 'I have listened to enough of her fine talk. But she shall talk no more. Kill her.' And Catherine was taken away to be put to death on a wheel.

We do not know exactly what sort of wheel it was, but we do know that it was a dreadful form of torture. Catherine was tied to it. Then, the people watching said, a remarkable thing happened. The wheel broke suddenly and quite unexpectedly, into a thousand shimmering pieces. Catherine was saved. But not for long. Emperor Maxentius was determined that she should die, and 12 days later she was beheaded.

Many years later Catherine was made a Saint and remembered as a very special person. She became the patron saint of spinners. Perhaps you know that in the olden days, girls would have a 'bottom drawer'. That meant they collected together all kinds of things they would need for their home, when they got married. They made clothes out of cloth they had woven and spun themselves. They used a spindle and later a spinning wheel to spin the wool into thread. Then they would weave the thread into cloth. These girls were called spinsters because of the spinning they did.

Many of them were very skilled at spinning. Sometimes young girls were sent to spinning schools. Just think, if you'd been a girl 200 hundred years ago, you might have been sent to a spinning school. If you had been, you would have looked forward very much to November 25th, Saint Catherine's Day, because then you would have been given a day off; a special holiday, in memory of Saint Catherine.

Catherine was a very brave girl to stand up for what she believed was right, when the Emperor Maxentius wanted to kill many poor people. We can try to be like her, and stand up for what we know is right, even though other people may not agree with us.

Prayer
Dear God, teach us to do what is right; to stand up for what is right; to work for what is right; even though it may not always be the easiest way.

Amen

Hymn
'Make me a channel of your peace' *Alleluya*

Practical ideas

Depending on the manual dexterity of the person taking the assembly, it may be possible to demonstrate to the children the way in which a distaff and spindle works. Most children will have a fair idea of what a spinning wheel looks like, from the story of Sleeping Beauty, even though they will have little comprehension of the way it works. A spindle is a simpler spinning device on which the raw wool is hooked. As the spindle is turned, the fibres are twisted together to form a continuous thread.

Further information can be found in the booklet *Wool Spinning*, by Hetty Wickens, published by Dryad (ISBN 85219 126 X); and *The National Trust book of Forgotten Household Crafts*, by John Seymour, published by Dorling Kindersley (ISBN 086 3181740).

Stir-up Sunday*   *Week 9   Advent*

*Stir-up Sunday is not actually in Advent, but since it has traditionally involved the stir up of Christmas puddings, it has been included in this week's theme. The collect for the day can be found in the Book of Common Prayer, under 'Collects, Epistles and Gospels for the twenty-fifth Sunday after Trinity'.

If you go to church on the fifth Sunday before Christmas, you will hear the vicar read a special prayer for the day. This prayer is called a collect and it starts,

'Stir up, we beseech thee, O Lord, the wills of they faithful people.'

That Sunday is called Stir-up Sunday, and is the day when lots of people used to make their Christmas puddings.

Sarah and David had gone to stay with their grandma and grandad for the weekend.

'What shall we do tomorrow?' they said on Saturday evening.

'That's easy,' said their grandma. 'We'll be busy tomorrow. There's a job to do. It's Stir-up Sunday.'

'What's that?' they both said. They'd never heard of Stir-up Sunday.

'When I was a little girl', their grandma said, 'I used to go to church every Sunday. Each Sunday has its own special prayer, and the special prayer for tomorrow tells the people to wake up, and get on, and do good things. But it's written in old-fashioned language and it tells the people to stir themselves up. 'Stir up, we beseech you' it says. My sister and I used to think it meant stir up the puddings, because our mum always made our Christmas puddings on stir-up Sunday.'

'Can we make a Christmas pudding?' asked David.

'That's exactly what we're going to do,' said his gran.

The next morning Sarah, David and their gran collected together all the ingredients they would need to make the Christmas pudding. They weighed out currants and raisins, suet and flour, nuts and peel and sugar and milk. They stirred in some salt, and whisked in some eggs, shook in some spices and squeezed in some orange and lemon juice.

'Can we have the brandy?' called their gran to Grandad. And he brought a glassful of brandy and a glassful of beer from the cupboard in the lounge. He tipped them into the mixture in the big mixing bowl.

'There!' said Gran. 'Now for the best bit.'

'I thought it was finished, now that it's all mixed,' said Sarah.

'No,' said Gran. 'Two more jobs to do.' And she opened a drawer in the kitchen cupboard and took out a small paper bag.

'Open that carefully,' she said to David.

David did as he was told and unwrapped the top of the bag where it was tightly folded over. He put his hand inside and felt some shapes that were small and hard.

'What is it?' asked Sarah.

'It's not an it, it's a they,' said David. 'There are lots of them.' And he tipped out seven tiny silver lucky charms, onto the kitchen table.

'Look there's a silver thimble, and a horseshoe.'

'There's an old-fashioned silver sixpence,' said Sarah, 'and a silver shoe and a silver horse.'

'And a flower and a car,' said David. 'Can I have the car, please, Gran? Go on, let me have the car. Please.'

'You can't choose which one to have,' said Gran. 'They're all to go in the pudding.'

'In the pudding?' said Sarah. 'You mean we put them in the pudding?'

'But of course,' said Gran. 'Then you'll have to wait until Christmas Day when we eat it, to see who gets which silver charm in their piece of pudding.'

She told the children to put the seven silver charms in the pudding, then Gran called to their grandad. 'Come on. It's time to stir up and wish!'

Grandad took hold of the big wooden spoon. He pushed it into the pudding mixture; it was stiff and thick.

'Now,' he said, 'you have to stir it three times from east to west, to remember the three wise men.' He stirred the pudding.

'Then you have to say:

'Stir up we beseech thee,

The pudding in the pot,

Because when it gets to Christmas Day,

We're going to eat the lot!" ' They all laughed.

'Then,' he said, 'you have to close your eyes and make a wish.' He shut his eyes tightly and looked as though he was thinking hard.

'What did you wish for Grandad?' said Sarah.

'You don't ask people what they've wished for, young lady. If you tell, it won't come true.'

Grandad handed the spoon to Sarah, and in turn, they all had a stir and a wish. Gran smiled as she finished her wish, and David jumped up and down and said 'I wish my wish'll come true.' But he wouldn't tell them what it was, in case it didn't.

When all the stirring and wishing was finished, Gran spooned the pudding mixture into a basin, and put it in a special steamer pan to cook.

Five weeks later, on Christmas Day, the pudding was steamed again and brought to the table. Gran carefully served it out. Sarah was busy telling her mum and dad all about how she and David had helped to make it, but David was digging in his pudding with his spoon.

'I've got it,' he shouted suddenly. 'The stir-up wish worked. Look!' And he lifted up something silvery on the end of his spoon.

Can you guess what David had wished for? I wonder what the others wished for when they stirred the pudding. Most people nowadays buy their Christmas pudding in a supermarket, but not so very long ago, everyone used to make their puddings, just like the children's grandma in the story.

Prayer

Thank you God, for all the good things we eat when we have celebrations.

Amen

Hymn

'We wish you a Merry Christmas' (*Carol, gaily carol*) or 'Thank you Lord' *Come and Praise* Vol 1

Practical ideas

With some preliminary preparation, a Christmas pudding can be successfully made during the assembly. I have involved children with the initial weighing of ingredients, then invited different children to mix the pudding in the assembly itself. Canteen staff were asked to help by steaming the pudding. 'Our' Christmas pudding was then produced on the day we ate our school Christmas dinner.

The Advent ring   *Week 9   Advent*

Advent Sunday is the fourth Sunday before Christmas. It comes at the end of November or the beginning of December and it is the beginning of the Christian year. Advent means coming, and Christians are waiting for the coming of Jesus' birthday at this time of year.

Lots of people have Advent calendars, with little windows to open each day. Some people make Advent rings and light a candle each week until Christmas Day. I'm going to tell you about the Advent ring today.

An Advent ring helps Christians to get ready for Christmas. It helps them to remember that Christmas isn't just about getting presents, but is about Jesus' birthday. I'd like some children to help me make our Advent ring.

I have a round tin tray and this is going to be the base of the ring. These children are going to make a circle of plasticine to fit inside the ring.

They are going to mark the positions of four candles round the edge of the ring, and one in the middle.

They are going to decorate the spaces that are left with evergreen leaves, fir cones, ribbons and baubles.

Now I'll show you where the candles go, and we'll put them into place. But we can't light them all yet. We are only allowed to light one the first week, two the second week, three the third week, and four the fourth week. When we have our last assembly on the day we break up for Christmas, we'll light all five candles.

Here's the first candle going into place. This candle stands for the Prophets. The Prophets were people who knew that God would send a special king to bring peace and love to the world. The prophets told everyone that God would send a king who would be honest and kind.

Here is the second candle going into place. This candle is to remind Christians about John the Baptist. John the Baptist was Jesus' cousin. He tried to make people ready for the day when Jesus would come, by asking them to say they were sorry to God, for all the wrong things they had done. Many of the people were baptised by John. That meant they used water to show they were trying to wash themselves clean, both inside and outside themselves. Then they tried to lead good lives whilst they waited for the new special king, Jesus, to come from God.

The third candle is for Mary, Jesus' mother. This candle reminds Christians how Mary prepared for Jesus to be born. Mary was very happy when she was told by the Angel Gabriel that she was to have a special baby – the son of God. She was so happy that she sang a song of praise. This song is called the Magnificat. It starts, 'My heart praises the Lord; my soul is glad because of God . . . he has remembered me.'

Here is the fourth candle. It stands for hope. We hope for many things every day, but Christians hope and believe that one day Jesus will come back again to help the people of our world. They hope that in the future our world will be a place where there is no wrong, but where everyone is honest and good.

And here is the last candle going into place. This is the biggest candle. The most important one. This candle stands for Jesus the King. Jesus the light of the world. Jesus who came to earth as a tiny baby, but who is the son of God. This tall candle sits in the middle of a never-ending circle (because a circle has no beginning and no end); a circle made of evergreens, to show that the love of God has no end.

As I have already said, we cannot light all the candles now, we must light them in turn, each week until Christmas. But today, it is the first week of Advent so we can light the first candle. The Prophet candle.

Prayer
Thank you God, for Christmas. This Advent, please help us to remember that Jesus came to the world to teach us to love one another. Please help us to remember to care for our family and friends.

Amen

Hymn
'Mary met an angel'   Carol, gaily carol

Practical ideas
This assembly would be incomplete without making an Advent ring with the children. The ring need not be elaborate, but the usual care should be taken when using candles and naked flames. If it is considered unsuitable to use real candles, a collage Advent ring can be very successful, and the children can be involved in the same way as described in the story text.

Biblical references to the theme   *Week 10   Friends*

'There are seven things that the Lord hates . . . and a man who stirs up trouble among friends.'

Proverbs 6:16-19

'If you want people to like you, forgive them when they wrong you. Remembering wrongs can break up a friendship.'

Proverbs 17:9

'Some friendships do not last, but some friends are more loyal than brothers.'

Proverbs 18:24

'An honest answer is a sign of true friendship.'

Proverbs 24:26

'But that is not all; we rejoice because of what God has done through our Lord Jesus Christ, who has now made us God's friends.'

Romans 5:11

'Dear friends, let us love one another, because love comes from God.'

1 John 4:7

The good kings
adapted from the Rājovāda Jātaka

Week 10: Friends

The other day two children at our school were fighting. When I asked them what the trouble was, the girl said that the boy had hit her first, so she had hit him back. Well, you can imagine what I said, because, as you know, we try not to fight at our school. We try to settle our differences peacefully, without hurting each other. We try to walk away if someone is annoying us, and if they continue to upset us, we find a grown-up to help us to sort out the problem.

A man once asked Jesus what to do if someone hit him. Jesus answered, 'Turn the other cheek'. Another man at another time asked the Buddha what to do, and he told his story.

There was once a time when everything was going well for King Brahmadatta of Benares. Everything seemed to be going so well that the king worried. Perhaps things were not really as good as he thought they were. Perhaps his people were not really very happy. Perhaps they were afraid to say what they really thought. King Brahmadatta decided to disguise himself as an ordinary man and to go out and about to find out what the people really thought of him.

Now it just so happened that another king, King Mallika of Kosala, had decided to do exactly that same thing as King Brahmadatta, at exactly the same time. Both kings were dressed as ordinary men, and both kings were travelling about the countryside in an ordinary horse and carriage. But King Brahmadatta was travelling south, and King Mallika was travelling north.

The two carriages met, head on, in a very narrow lane. There was no space for either to pass. One of the carriages would have to go back down the lane, to let the other one through.

King Mallika's driver said 'Get out of the way!'

'No,' said King Brahmadatta's driver, 'There's a king in this carriage. You'll have to get out of the way.'

'But there's a king in this carriage, too,' said King Mallika's driver.

'Then let the younger king give way to the older king,' said Brahmadatta's driver. 'That's fair. The younger one can show respect to the older.'

But when the two drivers spoke to the kings, it turned out that they were both born on exactly the same day. They were exactly the same age. Neither of them was older or younger than the other.

'Then let's see which has the biggest kingdom,' said Brahmadatta's driver. 'The king with the smaller kingdom can give way to the king with the larger one.'

The drivers brought out maps of their kings' land. They did complicated sums to work out exactly how many square metres each king controlled. They discovered . . . that each king had a kingdom of exactly the same size; the same number of houses, castles, palaces, people, farms, villages, towns, everything.

'Then we must decide which is the better king,' said Brahmadatta's driver. 'The king who is superior can stay put. The king who is inferior must go back down the lane and give way to the other.'

'That's easy,' said King Mallika's driver. 'My king is best. My king is a good king. He is fair and just. If people are good, he treats them well. If people are bad, he punishes them. He is a strong king.'

'My king is a good king too,' said King Brahmadatta's driver. 'He is fair and just. But he does things differently from your king. If people are good, he treats them well. And if people are bad . . . he still treats them well. He is a very strong king.'

At those words, King Mallika and his driver climbed down from their carriage, untied the horses, and pushed their carriage back down the lane, so that King Brahmadatta could go forward on his journey.

'I will give way to the better king,' said King Mallika. 'And I will try to learn from what you have said.'

King Mallika went back home again and tried to be fair and just. He treated good with good. And he treated those who were not so good, as well as he was able.

The next time someone is unkind to you, try not to be unkind back to them. Sometimes it's stronger *not* to fight back. And remember, two wrongs don't make a right! They make a twice-as-wrong!

Prayer

Dear God, when people are kind to us, help us be kind to them. When people are unkind to us, give us the strength still to be kind. Teach us to meet good with good, and overcome bad with good.

Amen

Hymn

'Down by the riverside' *Come and Praise* Vol 2

Mrs Hetherington
Week 10   Friends

I like getting letters and I have several pen-friends in different parts of the world. I look forward to the postman coming each day and seeing whether there's a letter for me from France or America or Romania. I've not met some of my pen-friends, and perhaps I never shall, but we're friends all the same. The friendships work because we take it in turns to write to each other. It wouldn't be any good if I just enjoyed *getting* the letters, and never sent any in return. To have a friend, you have to *be* a friend. That's the same for all friends, whether you write to them, or whether you see them every day. The person in today's story nearly didn't have a friend at all.

Mrs Hetherington had just moved house. She used to live in a big old house, which was fine when her husband and her family were there as well. But now there was just her. Her children had all grown up and moved away into houses of their own, and her husband sadly had died. Mrs Hetherington found a small new house and sold the big old one.

Moving house was hard work. There was a lot to do. First there had been all that packing at the old house, and now she was here at the new one, everything had to be unpacked again and put in its new place. Nothing seemed quite to fit where she wanted it to go. And all the jobs seemed to take such a long time.

While she was unpacking all her books and putting them in the bookcase, someone came to the door.

'Hello, I'm Mrs Wolenski,' said the someone. 'I'm your neighbour. I wondered if you'd like to come round for a cup of coffee. I know how tiring it is when you move house. Would you like to come?'

'No, thank you,' said Mrs Hetherington. 'It's very kind of you. But I've such a lot to do. Goodbye.' And she closed the door.

A little later there was another knock on the door.

'Hello, I'm Mr Patel. My wife and I are just going to the shops. We wondered if there's anything you want. We know how busy you must be, having just moved in. Is there anything we can get you?'

'No thank you,' said Mrs Hetherington. 'There's nothing I need at the moment. I must get on. I've such a lot to do. Goodbye.' And she closed the door. Mrs Hetherington carried on unpacking her boxes.

She worked all afternoon, and at tea-time there was another knock at the door. Mrs Hetherington answered it.

'Hello,' said the lady. 'I live in the house opposite, and I'm just going to have my tea. I know how busy you must have been today, just moving in, I wondered if you'd like to come and have your tea at my house. We could get to know each other.'

'No thank you,' said Mrs Hetherington. 'It's very kind of you. But I really haven't time. I've such a lot to do. Goodbye.' And she closed the door.

Mrs Hetherington worked hard for the next few days, sorting out her new house, and exactly one week after moving in, she had everything neat, tidy and just as she wanted it.

'There!' she said when it was all ready. 'Now I'm ready to have visitors. Now my new neighbours can come to see me.'

Mrs Hetherington got out her best cups and saucers and opened a packet of chocolate biscuits. Then she waited for her neighbours to call round to see her. She waited all that day in her neat and tidy house. She waited all the next day as well, and the day after that. But no-one came to see her. Mrs Hetherington began to feel quite lonely.

She decided that there was only one thing to do – she would have to go round and see them, if they were not going to come round and visit her. Mrs Hetherington put on her coat and hat and knocked on the door at Mrs Wolenski's, Mr and Mrs Patel's, and the house of the lady who lived opposite. She asked them all if they would like to come to her house for tea.

Everyone looked rather surprised, but they all said yes please. Later, much later, when Mrs Hetherington had lived in the new house for a long time, one of her new friends said how surprised they were that Mrs Hetherington had had that first tea party.

'Why's that?' she asked.

'Well,' said the neighbour, 'We all thought you were unfriendly. When you moved in on that first day, we all tried to help, but you didn't seem to want our help. We all thought you didn't want to be friends with us.'

'I'm sorry,' said Mrs Hetherington. 'I was just very busy. But I'm glad I'm not too busy to be friends now.'

Mrs Hetherington learned that if you want to have a friend, you need to be a friend. She could have been very lonely if she hadn't found that out. I hope the people in our school are never too busy to speak to their friends.

Prayer
Help us Lord, to have time for our friends. Make us never too busy to give a kind word or a helping hand. Help us to know that to *have* a friend, we must first *be* a friend.

Amen

Hymn
'Let the world rejoice together' *Come and Praise* Vol 2

Malin and Bon *Week 10 Friends*
adapted from the Panchatantra

I like to think that I am loyal to my friends. Being loyal means that you don't deliberately say or do anything to hurt your friends. If you're loyal to your friends, you stand by them if they need you; you don't do anything behind their back; you 'stick up' for them. If you are not loyal to your friends, they are not likely to want to be your friends for much longer.

Today's story is about two people who started off by being friends . . . but I'm glad one of them isn't a friend of mine! I think you'll be able to guess which one I mean.

Once upon a time two friends went travelling. Quite by chance they found a purse with a thousand silver coins in it. One of the friends, called Bon, said they should take it to the police, so that it could be given back to its owner. The other friend, called Malin, was not so sure about doing this, but in the end he agreed. The purse was handed in. Much later, when the friends travelled that way again, they called in to see if the purse had been collected by its owner. They were very surprised when the police said they couldn't find who it belonged to, and since that was the case, the two friends could have it to keep.

Bon and Malin were delighted. A thousand silver coins. For them. To keep. They danced down the street then sat on a wall to decide what to do with it.

'Let's just share it in half and go home,' said Bon. 'We can tell all our friends about our good luck.'

'No,' said Malin, who didn't want *half* the money – he wanted most of it. 'No. Let's go home, but let's just have a hundred pieces each and let's bury the rest somewhere safe. Then we can get some more whenever we need it.'

'All right,' said Bon. So the two friends took a hundred silver coins each, went home together, and buried the eight hundred silver coins under a large tree near their houses.

After a while Malin had spent all his money. He was about to go to Bon and ask if they could have another hundred coins each, when he thought of a plan that would give him more than his share. He went to the tree, dug up all the money, put it in his pockets, put the soil back, and went home. Then, he went to see Bon.

'Bon,' he said, 'I need some more money. Can we have another hundred coins each? Will you come with me and dig them up? I want us both to be there, so that we know it's fair!'

'Of course,' said Bon, and the two of them went to the tree to dig up the coins. But of course, they were not there.

'Oh no!' said Malin. 'Someone must have stolen them. How dreadful! But no-one knew they were there, except YOU. YOU must have stolen the coins. Oh, Bon, how could you do this to me? You must pay me back half the coins you have taken. I want them now.'

'Malin, I didn't take the silver. I wouldn't steal from you. It must have been someone else.'

'It can't have been anyone else. Only YOU knew where the coins were hidden. Give me my share back.'

Soon the quarrelling grew so loud that Malin and Bon were called before the judge, whose job it was to sort out the argument. But the judge found it hard to decide who was telling the truth. Meanwhile, Malin had thought of another plan.

'I know how we can sort all this out,' he shouted, 'I know who saw it all and who can tell us the truth. The tree saw it all. The tree can tell you that I am telling the truth'.

Everyone stared at Malin in amazement.

'The tree?' said the judge.

'The tree?' said Bon.

'The tree!' answered Malin. 'Come and stand by the tree tomorrow. It will tell you that Bon stole my money.'

Then Malin went home to his father's house. He told him about the money and said that his father must go and hide himself in the tree, and pretend to be the voice of the tree, and say that it was Bon who stole the money.

'I can't do that,' said Malin's father. But Malin forced him to the tree and made him stand inside it all night.

In the morning everyone gathered round the tree to hear it speak.

'Who stole the money?' asked the judge.

'Bon stole the money,' answered the voice of the tree.

'That is not true,' shouted Bon, and before anyone could stop him, he ran across to the tree and climbed up it to see what he could see.

'Ah!' he said. 'Here is the voice of the tree!' and he poked poor Malin's father out of the hollow trunk with a burning stick.

'Owww!' shouted the voice of the tree. 'It isn't my fault. I didn't want to do it. He made me,' and Malin's father told everyone all that Malin had told him the night before.

The judge made Malin give back all the money to Bon. He said that Malin wasn't to have even his own share; Bon must have it all in compensation for having such a disloyal friend.

I don't know whether Malin and Bon stayed friends after that. I wonder what *you* would have done, if *your* friend had been as dishonest and disloyal to you, as Malin was to Bon. Do you think Bon should have forgiven him and stayed friends?

Prayer

Dear God, help us to be loyal to our friends. Help us not to cheat when we play games together. Help us to do nothing to hurt our friends. Help us to know that friends are very valuable people and must be looked after.

Amen

Hymn

'Shalom' *Come and Praise* Vol 2

Bibilical references to the theme   *Week 11   Winter*

'Lazy people should learn a lesson from the way ants live. They have no leader, chief, or ruler, but they store up their food during the summer, getting ready for winter.'

Proverbs 6:6-8

'Be glad, people of Zion, rejoice at what the Lord your God has done for you. He has given you the right amount of autumn rain; he has poured down the winter rain for you and the spring rain as before.'

Joel 2:23

The wren   *Week 11   Winter*

Have you had any Christmas cards yet? I've noticed how many of mine
have snow scenes and wintry pictures on them. I've had, and sent, lots of
cards with robins on the front. I like robins; we sometimes think of them as
our national bird.

Robins and other birds have a hard time of it in winter. There's not much
food available for them and often they die of thirst because all the water
outside is frozen. We can help to keep garden birds alive by giving them
food and water in winter time, especially when the weather is really bad.

Very tiny birds find winter-time even more difficult than bigger birds,
because they lose their body heat more quickly. One of our country's
smallest birds is the wren – perhaps you've seen one, although they are
very shy. If you have a hedge in your garden, try to keep a bit of ground
under it clear of snow; the wrens will be able to scrape for food. Sometimes
in winter-time, wrens move in to old nesting boxes, and huddle together to
keep warm. There's a true story of a man, one winter, looking in to an old
nesting box in a tree in his garden, and finding 61 wrens, all crowded
together in there, where they were sheltered and warm.

In the spring-time, wrens make the most beautiful nests, and there's a
legend about why that's so.

Way, way back at the beginning of time, the birds were given lessons in
how to build their nests. They all sat in front of The Great One and they
listened to what they had to do.

But they listened, of course, in different ways. Perhaps you have noticed
that when someone is telling someone else how to do a thing; some listen
well, and others not so well!

The blackbird and sparrow listened quite well for most of the time. The
cuckoo didn't listen at all, to a single word. The owl and the pigeon listened
for some of the time, but then dozed and fell asleep. The most attentive of all
was the wren. He listened carefully to every word The Great One spoke.

After the lesson, the birds were sent out into the fields and woods to
build a sample nest.

The blackbird and sparrow made a fair attempt. Their nests passed the
test.

The cuckoo could not even begin. She would wait; she would not trouble
to make a nest of her own; what a waste of time! She would simply use the
nest of another bird. In fact, she would let another bird bring up her child.
So she sat and watched the others.

The owl and the pigeon made scrappy affairs; nests The Great One was
ashamed to see.

But the wren worked and worked. He made one, then another, then another nest again. He invited his wife to look, to choose, to decide, which she would have. She chose: and lined it most carefully with the finest and softest of her feathers. This nest was the best of all. The ones she had not chosen stood empty. Later, other creatures looking for homes found the empty cock nests. A bumble bee moved in to one, and a mouse used the other as her winter house.

The Great One saw all this happen. He looked at the test nests of the birds and decided to give no more lessons. They had each made the nest he knew they would make. After all, he had watched them in their lessons. He knew which had listened and which had not. And here was the proof.

If you're ever lucky enough to see a wren's nest, you will know how carefully it was made. Remember never to touch a bird's nest, or damage it in any way. And remember, if you can, to feed the birds this winter-time, so that they will live through the winter and be able to build their nests in the spring.

Prayer
Thank you God, for all the birds who live near our homes and our school. Help us to remember to feed them and give them water, when the weather is bad and they cannot easily care for themselves.

Amen

Hymn
'Little birds in winter time' *Someone's Singing, Lord*

Practical ideas
Prior to this assembly I made a display of various types of bird feeder, together with different kinds of bird food that I knew the children would either already have at home, or that was easy to obtain locally. I included some bird books and posters of common garden birds. The display was discussed at the end of the assembly, and then left where children could investigate it further in their own time.

Posters and information about birds can be obtained from the RSPB (Royal Society for the Protection of Birds), The Lodge, Sandy, Bedfordshire SG19 2DL.

Schools may also be interested in joining the Young Ornithologists Club, which is run by the RSPB. The Club publishes a colour magazine *Bird Life* six times a year.

The slide

I asked some children this morning if they like the winter and most of them said yes, they did. They said they like winter because they like snow, ice, Christmas, Diwali, Hanukkah, dark nights and winter food. Someone said that television is better in winter than in summer.

I haven't had a chance this morning, to ask any old people if *they* like winter, but I think I can guess what most of them would say. Can you? Most older people don't like winter, for the same reasons that you *do* like it! They don't like the weather in winter, and often they don't like winter festivals either; winter festivals can make people feel lonely if they don't have families around them.

Mrs Gill looked out of her window the week before Christmas, and felt very miserable. It was snowing again. It had snowed for three days now, and she had put off going out to the shops because she was afraid that if she went out she might fall. She didn't walk very well these days, and if she did fall and hurt herself, there was no-one to look after her.

Serena and Ben looked out of their window, and felt very excited. Their dad had promised them that if it snowed for three days, he would buy them a sledge. Today was the third day of the snow.

'Can we go get it now,' shouted Ben. His dad laughed and said yes.

They piled into the car and slithered along the roads to the supermarket. They chose a wooden sledge with shiny black runners.

'And share it,' said their dad, 'I'll not have any arguing about whose turn it is. I know you two.'

'We will,' they said, and pulled the sledge back to the car.

Mrs Gill looked out of her window again.

'It's no good,' she said. 'Snow or no snow, I'll have to go out to the shops. I'll be all right if I go slowly and take care.' She put on her boots and hat and coat, and collected her shopping bag. She carefully stepped out of her back door and gingerly walked down the garden path. It was very slippery. 'Oh dear!' she said. She tried to hold on to things as she passed them – the clothes post, a tree, the garden gate. She went through the gate and onto the pavement. Here there was less to hold on to. She trod slowly, carefully putting one foot down at a time.

Serena and Ben were having a great time. The drive of their house sloped down to the pavement, and was good as a toboggan run. They shared the sledge well to begin with, then Serena, who was bigger and older, wanted more turns. They argued, as their dad knew they would. Serena flounced off in a temper.

'Well, see if I care. You can keep the stupid sledge. I'm going to make a slide of my own, and *you* can't go on it.'

She went down the drive, on to the pavement and started to slide. She ran and slid, over and over again. She was very good at it and never once fell. The slide became glassy and hard. It shone and sparkled in the sunlight.

'You shouldn't do that there. Dad says so,' called Ben. 'You're not to make slides on the pavement, someone might fall.'

'Good. I hope it's you,' shouted Serena, and she carried on sliding.

Mrs Gill was doing quite well. She began to feel not so afraid of the snow and ice. After all, lots of people were out and about and they weren't falling down all over the place. She looked around her. Everything did look pretty in the sunshine. Everything was sparkling and clean-looking. She was walking a little more quickly now, but still carefully, one foot down, one foot up, tread, tread.

Serena was just at the end of her long slide when she heard the shout. Ben again. She wished he'd shut up. Little brothers were a noisy nuisance. He shouted again. She turned, too quickly this time, and fell down hard on the shimmering shining ice slide. As she fell she noticed a lady, quite an old lady, almost stepping on to the beginning of the slide, but Ben had shouted to her to stop. Lucky thing she'd taken notice of what he'd said. Serena put her hands round her ankle. It hurt.

Their dad came hurrying out of the house, 'Are you all right?' he asked Mrs Gill. 'And what about you?' he said to Serena. 'I think we'd better all go inside.'

And the story ends there. I wonder what happened next? Perhaps the family tried to help Mrs Gill. Maybe they did all her shopping for her, or cleared her garden of snow. I wonder if Serena's dad was very cross with her for making a slide on the pavement. I think I would have been! It's a pity that Serena didn't think a bit more carefully before she made her slide, but I'm glad it didn't cause Mrs Gill to have an accident. Serena wasn't badly hurt, but if Mrs Gill had fallen she could have broken her leg or hip, and been in hospital a very long time.

I hope that when you enjoy the winter weather, you don't do anything which might cause anyone else to get hurt.

Prayer
Thank you God, for winter. Thank you for winter weather and winter fun. Help us to look after people who might not enjoy the winter. Help us to think before we play, so that we don't cause accidents.

Amen

Hymn
'The best gift'   *Come and Praise* Vol 1

Hannah Hauxwell   *Week 11   Winter*

Some people like winter; some people don't. All people have to put up
with it whether they like it or not. They have to 'like it or lump it' as my
mum would say. The lady in today's story had no choice but to put up with
the winter, even though she didn't like it. But, even though her life was
very hard, she didn't complain or grumble. Today's story is true.

One winter, a television film maker went to Yorkshire to make a
programme about people living on hill farms in winter. He found a road
that led to a lonely and isolated Dale and followed it. When the road
turned into a track, he followed that. And when the track turned into a
path, he followed that. When the path itself disappeared into the frosty
grass of a field, the man decided that he was too far away from anywhere to
go any further, and that it was time to turn back.
    'There can be no-one living here,' he said to himself. 'It is too wild and
lonely.'
    He was just about to turn round and find his way down the hillside again,
when he thought he saw something move. He wasn't very certain, because
it was by now quite difficult to see. It was nearly dark and the wind was
whipping up a blizzard of snow. The man stood still and peered into the
gloom.
    There, in front of him, walked a woman. She was bent against the wind
and snow, she was dressed in a collection of old and patched clothes, and
she was leading a large white cow at the end of a piece of rope. She saw the
man and said 'Good afternoon.' Then she trudged across the field to a long
low building and disappeared inside. The man had found Hannah
Hauxwell.
    She lived all alone in an old farm house deep in the hills. She had hardly
any money to live on, and the little she had also had to pay for food for her
cows. Once every month she walked a mile and a half up the hill to the
road, and collected a cardboard box from the wall. This box was delivered
to the wall by the shopkeeper in the village, and it contained always the
same things – some butter, eggs and sugar, some tomatoes and onions, a
lump of cheese and some bread. It was all that Hannah could afford.
    Every day, she had to take an old tin bucket and walk down the hill to
the stream to collect some water. She had no taps in the house, the only
water she had was from the stream that the cattle used. In the winter the

stream would freeze over and she would have to collect pieces of ice and then melt them in her house. But even that was not easy. Hannah had no gas or electricity in the house. She had no central heating. Sometimes she managed to have a fire lit in the grate, but there was not much wood to be found on the farm, and she couldn't afford to buy coal. And even if there'd been money to buy it, there was no road to her house, and no-one would have been able to deliver it.

The man asked Hannah if she would mind having a television film made about her, so that everyone could see what life was like on a lonely hill farm. Hannah was surprised. She couldn't imagine why anyone should want to watch a film about her. But the man felt sure they would. He felt sure that millions of people all over Britain would learn something from this quiet, content, lady. For although Hannah was without a doubt one of the poorest people in the whole of the country, she was not miserable, or complaining, or unhappy, or grumbling. She was not cross, or angry that she had so little. She did not blame anyone for her life being as poor as it was. She did not lose her temper and shout, when life was so difficult it was almost unbearable. She had a certain calm and peace about her.

The film was shown. It was called 'Too long a winter'. When the programme had finished, thousands of people rang the television company to say how much they had enjoyed it. Newspapers carried stories about Hannah. And in time, two more television programmes were made about her. Books were written about Hannah, and many, many people sent her gifts and money to make her life easier.

The film was made 20 years ago. Hannah no longer lives in her lonely hill farm. She had to leave it because she became unable to manage there all alone. Her new friends were afraid that she might die one cold hard winter, and that no-one would be with her or near her to help. She was very sad to leave her home in the Dale, and especially sad to leave her animals. She says she will never go back, even to visit the farm. But she has not moved far away. She lives now in a village further down her Dale; a village that is in gentler countryside, where there are people who can help her if she becomes ill.

Our world would be a much better place if there were more people in it like Hannah: people who try to be calm and peaceful, even if they find things difficult. People who help others to feel quiet and calm, because of the way they are.

Prayer

Dear God, Please help all the people who live in lonely, isolated places. Please help all the people who find winter-time difficult. Please help us to accept the things we cannot change, calmly and without anger.

Amen

Hymn
'To ev'rything, turn'   *Come and Praise* Vol 2

Practical ideas
Three books by Barry Cockcroft contain photographs of Hannah Hauxwell, and of a bygone way of life in the Yorkshire Dales. I made the books available to children, especially the older ones, after this assembly, and several children were inspired to do further work on 'life before modern gadgets'. The photographs of Hannah brought her character alive to the younger children. The books are: *Hannah in Yorkshire* published by Dalesman Books (ISBN 0 85206 452 7); *Seasons of my Life* published by Century (ISBN 07126 24805); *Daughter of the Dales* published by Century (ISBN 07216 45004).

Biblical references to the theme   Week 12   Christmas

'She gave birth to her first son, wrapped him in strips of cloth and laid him in a manger – there was no room for them to stay in the inn.'

Luke 2:7

'Soon afterwards, some men who studied the stars came from the east to Jerusalem and asked, "Where is the baby born to be the king of the Jews? We saw his star when it came up in the east, and we have come to worship." '

Matthew 2:1-2

'Joseph got up, took the child and his mother, and left during the night for Egypt, where he stayed until Herod died.'

Matthew 2:14-15

The cluttered room   Week 12   Christmas
adapted from Jewish teaching

I wonder how many of you will be having presents soon? Some children have presents in December because it's Christmas; others because it's Diwali; others because it's Hanukkah; and yet others because they have a birthday this month. Sometimes people end up with so many presents they don't know what to do with them. Here's a story about a man who had a very cluttered room, which became even more crowded when he was given some presents. The story has a strange ending!

Once upon a time there was a very poor man, who lived with his wife and family in a tiny house with just one room. The room was so small that the man and woman and children were always falling over each other and getting in each other's way.

One day the man went to see the rabbi. 'I can't stand it in my house,' said the man. 'We're always in each other's way. Tell me what to do.'

'I'll give you a dog,' said the rabbi. 'It'll help.'

But the dog didn't help. In fact it made everything worse. It was a very big dog and it barked a lot and knocked things over with its tail.

The man went back to see the rabbi. 'Thank you for your present, but I'm afraid it hasn't helped. Things are just as bad as before.'

'Don't worry,' said the rabbi. 'I have something else.' And he gave the man some hens.

Well, the gift of the hens was disastrous. They flapped and flew all over the man's house. They frightened the baby and made a dreadful mess on everything.

'I'm sorry,' said the man. 'I know you were trying to help, but the situation is getting worse by the minute. The hens haven't helped at all.'

'No?' said the rabbi. 'Then try this.' And he gave the man a goat.

'A goat?' said the man, 'That's not going to do any good.'

'Take it home and see.'

The man took the goat home and the whole situation became impossible.

Then the rabbi turned up with a donkey. 'I've brought you another present,' he said.

The next day he came to the house with a horse!

'This'll do the trick,' said the rabbi. 'This will solve your problem.'

'No!' shouted the man. 'Thank you, but no.'

'No?' said the rabbi.

'No!' said the man.

'Then get rid of them all,' said the rabbi. 'Get rid of them all, then tell me how you feel. I'll come back again tomorrow.'

The rabbi went away and the man set about finding homes for all the animals the rabbi had given him. By evening it was done. By morning the man felt so much better. The rabbi called again.

'Well, how do you feel?' he asked.

'I feel wonderful,' said the man. 'I can't begin to tell you how good I feel. Yesterday evening my wife and children and I had the whole room to ourselves. We had so much space. We had so much freedom. it's a lovely house when we've got it all to ourselves. Thank you for helping us.'

'It's a pleasure,' said the rabbi. 'Glad I was able to help.'

Did you like the end of the story? The man of course, had the same at the end of the story as he had at the beginning, but it took all those animals to make him see that. Perhaps the one present we all need, is one to get rid of all the others!

Prayer

Thank you God, for all the things we are given. Help us to know that getting presents doesn't make happiness. Help us to share what we have with other people who don't have as much as we do.

Amen

Hymn

'What shall I give to the child in the manger?'   *Carol, gaily carol*

Follow the star   *Week 12   Christmas*
adapted from the Bible

Our school looks lovely just now, with all its Christmas decorations. One of my favourite decorations is the Christmas tree, with its baubles and lights and its tinsel and star. Some people put a fairy at the top of the tree, instead of a star, but I like stars best; they remind people of the star that the wise men followed, that very first Christmas.

The man who saw it first called to the others to come and look.
'I've read about a new star like that,' he said. 'It means the birth of a new king.'
'I've read that too,' said another. 'I think we should follow it. It'll lead us to the palace where the king is born.'
The men prepared for their journey; they knew it might be long. They took with them precious presents to give to the new king. Presents, fit for a king, of gold, frankincense and myrrh. They set off on their journey and followed the star. It glittered and glistened and sparkled before them, and showed them the way.
Soon they came to the city of Jerusalem.
'Here's a likely place for a king,' they said. 'Here's a golden palace. Here's where he'll be.'
But he was not. There was no baby here. This was Herod's palace.
'A baby king!' shouted Herod. 'Here? I think not. I am king here.' Then he changed his voice and spoke softly, 'But go and find him please. And when you have found him, come and tell me, so that I can go and worship him too,' and Herod smiled.

The men travelled further, on to Bethlehem, following the star, until it stopped over the stable.

'It can't be here,' they said. 'Here is a poor place. A king will not be born here.' But they went inside and found him, with Mary his mother and Joseph.

The men knelt down and worshipped the new baby, and presented him with their gifts: gold; frankincense; myrrh.

Afterwards, they prepared to set off again to their own country.

'We must go and tell King Herod we have found the new baby,' they said. 'We must call in at his palace in Jerusalem.' But that night the men had a dream in which they were told not to go and see King Herod. 'He means harm to the baby,' they said later. 'We'll go home a different way, and then he'll not see us. We will not tell him where the baby is.'

And the men went home a different way.

But King Herod didn't give up so easily. He was a jealous king and couldn't bear to think that a new baby might grow up and take over his job. King Herod was determined to find the new baby. I'll tell you the rest of the story tomorrow. In the meantime, the star on the top of our tree will remind you of the story of the star that led wise men to Bethlehem.

Prayer

Dear God, thank you for all the stars in the sky. Thank you for their mystery and majesty. Thank you for the special star which led the wise men to the stable, that first Christmas-time.

Amen

Hymn

'Little star'   *Come and Praise* Vol 2

To Egypt

Week 12   Christmas

an adaptation of a Biblical story and a legend

Yesterday I told you the story of the wise men, and how the star on the top of a tree reminds us of that story. Today I am going to tell you the next part of the story, and there is a reminder on our tree of this, as well.

One night, soon after the wise men had left the stable to go back to their own country, Joseph had a dream. He dreamed that Herod was looking for the baby and wanted to kill him. In the dream, Joseph was told to take Mary and the baby to a land called Egypt, where they would be safe.

Joseph got up early the next morning and told Mary of his dream.

'We must set off straight away,' he said. 'I am sure the dream was a message from God. We must do as he says, otherwise some harm might come to Jesus.'

Mary and Joseph gathered their things together and set off for Egypt.

Meanwhile, Herod was waiting in his palace for the men from the east to come back and tell him where the new baby was.

He was getting impatient. He seemed to have been waiting a long time.

'Surely they should be here by now,' he said to his men. 'It can't take all this time to find a new baby.'

Herod waited and waited.

Then a message came from some villagers to say that they had seen the eastern men going home a different way. The men had not called in to see Herod.

King Herod was furious.

'They shall pay for this,' he said. 'They shall all pay. Herod is king and will continue to be so. I will not be displaced by a baby. Kill them.'

His men at first did not understand.

'Kill them,' said Herod. 'Kill all the baby boys. Every one. Every single one that is in or near Bethlehem and that is two years old or younger. Kill them.'

His men did not dare to disobey.

There is a story which tells of Joseph, Mary and the baby running away from the soldiers of King Herod. The story says they heard the footsteps of the soldiers behind them and ran into a cave to hide. They stayed quite still. The baby didn't cry.

The soldiers searched everywhere and two of them came right up to the entrance of the cave. They looked inside. One of the soldiers said 'This would be a good place to hide, they could be in here. Let's go in and look.' But the other soldier said. 'Don't be silly. They couldn't be in here. Look at all these spiders' webs across the entrance. There's hundreds of them, all silvery with dust. No-one's been in here for years. If they'd tried to get in here these webs would be all broken and torn. Come on. Let's go and search somewhere else.' And the soldiers went away, leaving Joseph, Mary and the baby safely hidden in the cave.

The story says that spiders wove the webs when Mary, Joseph and the baby were hiding in the cave, just so that the soldiers would think that no-one was inside. In that way the three of them were saved. The tinsel we hang on our Christmas trees is to remind people of the story of the silvery spiders' webs that saved the baby.

Joseph, Mary and the baby reached Egypt safely and stayed there until

King Herod died. When that happened, Joseph had another dream. He was told that it was safe to return to the land of Israel. He, Mary and the child (for Jesus was by then no longer a baby) set off for home.

Prayer
Thank you God, for Christmas. Thank you for Christmas decorations, Christmas presents, Christmas fun and Christmas happiness. Please help everyone to find happiness and peace this Christmas-time.

Amen

Hymn
'There were three kings'   *Carol, gaily carol*

Practical ideas
I always make a display of Christmas books for the children to read for themselves. Some books they have particularly enjoyed, and which have excellent illustrations, include;

Christmas by Jan Pienkowski, published by Heinemann,
   ISBN 0 434 95649 X.
A Christmas Story by Brian Wildsmith, published by Oxford University
   Press, ISBN 0 19 272244 1.
The Story of Christmas by Jane Ray, published by Orchard Books,
   ISBN 1 85213 280 9.
The Christmas Book by Dick Bruna, published by Methuen Children's
   Books, ISBN 0 416 24170 0.
The Nativity illustrated by Juan Wijngaard, published by Walker Books,
   ISBN 0 7445 2039 8.
Silent Night by Francesca Crespi, published by Methuen Children's Books,
   ISBN 0 416 01482 8.

I have also found the *Oxford Book of Christmas Poems* a valuable resource (ISBN 0 19 276080 7).

Spring Term

Biblical references to the theme   *Week 1   Each day different*

'So do not worry about tomorrow; it will have enough worries of its own. There is no need to add to the troubles each day brings.'

Matthew 6:34

'Let lights appear in the sky to separate day from night and to show the time when days, years, and religious festivals begin.'

Genesis 1:14

Balloons   *Week 1   Each day different*

Happy New Year everyone! I hope you've all enjoyed your holiday, and that you helped your family to have a happy holiday too.

There were some exciting days over Christmas weren't there? Of course there were some days which were not so exciting as well. I wonder if you had any days during the holiday when you felt bored or fed-up or didn't know what to do? Sometimes there are days like that when you think nothing interesting is going to happen. But you never know what might turn up!

My friend Rosa is about the same age as some of you. One day just after Christmas she felt really bored. She'd opened all her presents, played with her games, read two of her books, done three jig-saws, eaten all her selection box, visited her cousins and some of her friends . . . and now she was BORED.

'Mum. I've nothing to do,' she said.

'Play with your toys,' said her mum. But Rosa didn't want to.

She went upstairs to her bedroom and looked out of the window. It was a grey, dismal, dreary day. Rosa heaved a great sigh, propped her elbows on the window-sill and stuck her chin in her hands.

Suddenly, way over on the horizon, she saw something move. It was big and bright and round. Rosa stared in astonishment. Another large spherical shape like a ball crept up over the horizon, then another and another. By now the first ball had floated nearer, and because it was nearer it seemed bigger, and Rosa could see that it wasn't a ball at all. It had a square shape hanging underneath it and something else that kept whooshing roaring tongues of flame into it.

'It's a hot air balloon!' said Rosa.

She rushed downstairs to tell her mum and together they went out into the garden. Lots of their neighbours had seen the balloons as well and they were all outside watching them.

The first of the balloons were over the field at the bottom of the row of gardens by now. They were so near that Rosa could see the people inside the baskets quite clearly. She waved and shouted to them and the people waved back and shouted 'Happy New Year!'

Just then, one of the balloons seemed to be having some difficulty in staying up high in the sky. It floated lower and lower and only just skimmed the top of the hedge at the far side of the field.

'It's going to crash,' whispered Rosa. 'Will the people get hurt, Mum?' But before her mum had time to answer, the balloon's basket bumped and banged and buffeted its way along the tuffety grass of the field. The people inside were jolted and jarred but they weren't hurt.

'And I always thought ballooning was a very gentle thing to do,' said Rosa's mum. 'It's not quite the gentle sport I thought it was!'

One of the women in the basket then pulled a lever on the gas cylinder and a mighty roar of flame gushed into the mouth of the balloon. Slowly the huge balloon regained its height and floated away over the roof of Rosa's house. The neighbours stood and watched until the last of the balloons had disappeared behind the houses.

'Let's all go inside and have coffee and mince pies,' someone said. And so that's what they all did. And they all had a lot to talk about.

Rosa's boring day turned out to be an exciting one after all. If you think you're having a dull, uninteresting day some time, just keep your eyes open, you never know what you might see!

Prayer
Please help us to find something cheerful in every day. Help us to remember that yesterday has gone, tomorrow is not yet here, *today* is the day that matters. Help us to make the best of today.

Amen

Hymn
'This is the day'   *Alleluya*

Practical ideas
A display of pictures, reference books and photographs of hot-air balloons could be made, prior to the assembly. (Montgolfier, Blanchard and Jeffries are names to research regarding the development of ballooning. January 7th 1785 saw the first air crossing of the English Channel, by hot-air balloon.) Follow-up work can be linked to English, science, history, art and technology.

The months of the year

I know that you know the names of the days of the week; but can you tell me the names of the months of the year? (Children recite the months in order.) I knew you could do it! But did you know that they were not always in that order? Did you know that once upon a time they couldn't decide which order to be in at all, and the world was in a dreadful state?

Long, long ago, before the beginning of time proper, the months of the year were not in the order they are today. In fact they were not in any order and they used to change themselves about whenever they felt like it. Sometimes July would come after December, or before January, or even in the middle of April, just depending how he felt at the time. So there was no order in the world because no-one ever knew when anything was going to happen.

Not only that, but the months didn't even have the same sort of weather each time they had a turn. Can you imagine it? Sometimes November would be hot and sunny, and August would have snow and hailstorms. Then the next time around they might change their minds and swap their weather . . . or they might not . . . as the case may be.

No-one knew where they were. It was impossible to plan ahead, the animals never knew when to hibernate and the birds didn't know when to migrate and when to fly home again. And as for the people, they never knew what to wear. They didn't know from one day to the next whether to get out their summer sandals or their winter woollies.

Even the months themselves didn't like the haphazard chaos.

'This is no good,' they said. 'We'll have to sort ourselves out. We'll have to have a system so that everyone knows where they are.'

'Good idea,' said someone else. 'We need to choose a king month, a month to be in charge, a month to lead us.'

'We'll have a meeting,' they decided, 'So that we can arrange ourselves into some sort of order and make the world a better place.'

And so the months of the year met together at the appointed time and place and sat in a circle to begin the meeting.

January thought they should first of all decide what kind of weather they were each going to have.

November didn't think so, but didn't know why.

August thought it was a good idea to choose some weather each, and then everyone would know what to expect.

November said it was a silly idea.

June said it would be a good idea if they all chose some weather and then put all the cold months together and all the hot ones together.

November said no.

January asked them each to choose what weather they wanted.

And so all the months began to choose. They were all helpful and no month was being awkward or difficult or selfish. Except, of course, for November, who talked all the way through the meeting, but didn't actually say anything sensible.

January was very patient with him and tried not to get cross, but it was no use, they couldn't go ahead with the meeting because of all the interruptions from November.

'This is no use,' said January at last, 'We're getting nowhere. We will ask the owl to help us. He's sitting in that tree and has been watching us all the time.

'Will you help us, Owl?'

The owl slowly turned his head to face the circle of months.

'I think you, January, should be the leader of the year. You are sensible and thoughtful and helpful. It is right that the job should be yours. You November, have no brains, no sense, no patience, no thought, no consideration, no control. You should go to the end of the year. Not the very end, of course, that is a special place, reserved for a special month.

'Because you are silly and chattery, you will be a 'No' month.

No sun, no moon,

No morning, no noon,

No proper time of day.

No butterflies, no bees,

No leaves on trees.

No. . .vember!'

And so November became a rather dull, dreary, dismal sort of month, full of rain and fog and not much else.

The other months put themselves into order with January as their leader. February and March chose to be cold and blowy months. April and May wanted to start the spring. June, July and August decided to be summer, and September chose to be a warm, harvest month. October wanted to prepare for winter. November we know about! December chose the special job of finishing off the year with winter celebrations.

And of course, it's been that way ever since. Poor old November was punished for being silly, chattery and generally unhelpful.

Prayer

Thank you God for all the different months, and all the different days in them. Help us to be sensible and thoughtful in them all. Help us to use our voices sensibly and not in a silly, chattery way.

Amen

Hymn
'Days of the months'   *Harlequin*

Practical ideas
You could read the poem 'November' by Thomas Hood, to the older children.

Plough Monday   *Week 1   Each day different*

Every day is different, isn't it, and some days are special. Special days are special for different reasons: party days are special, holidays are special and birthdays are special. Sometimes your class does something unusual on a particular day, and that makes that day special for all your class to remember. Today's story is about a girl who went on a class visit, so that was special, but she found out about another special day that people used to celebrate many years ago.

One day in January a class of children went on a school visit to a museum of working horses in Yorkshire. They had been working on a topic about horses. Today they were visiting the museum to see some of the machinery and carts and carriages that the horses used to pull, before the days of cars and lorries, tractors and buses.

When the children arrived at the museum they were met by a young man called Malcolm, a horse called Megan, lots of cats, and an old man called Seth. The children were told that after lunch they would have a ride on a bus pulled by Megan, and be taken on the canal on a barge also pulled by Megan. Megan would be wearing her best ribbons and bobbins for the barge trip, said Malcolm. But first the children were all going inside the museum itself to see some of the machinery that horses like Megan used to pull every day of their working lives.

The children went in to the long building and Malcolm began to tell them about the ploughs they could see.

'I wish we could have a ride with Megan *now*,' whispered one of the girls to her friend. 'This is boring.'

'It wasn't boring if you were a lad in my day,' said a voice behind her. She looked round and there was Seth, standing right behind her. The girl felt embarrassed that the old man had heard her. She hadn't meant to be rude about the museum.

'I just meant I wish we could miss this bit out and go and have a ride with Megan now,' she said.

'Miss out the ploughs!' said Seth. 'I bet you don't even know it's Plough Monday today, do you?'

'I've never heard of it,' said the girl.

'Well!' said Seth. 'Plough Monday is always the first Monday after the 6th of January. In the old days us children used to have a grand time on Plough Monday.'

'What did you do?' asked the girl.

'We had to get the ground ready,' said Seth. 'Ready for the next lot of seeds to be sown. It was our first festival of the New Year.

'We used to borrow bits of ribbon from our mother's sewing basket, and tie them all over ourselves. Then we used to put a paper mask on our face, and tie an old piece of leather over our back like a cloak.

'Then, when we were all dressed up we used to pull an old iron plough, just like this one here, all up and down the fields. We used to go right round the village, singing and dancing as we went, knocking at all the doors of the houses to tell everyone that we were there. Not that they needed much telling, mind, with all the noise we used to make.'

'But what was it for?' asked the girl.

'What for?' said Seth. 'To pull the badness out of the earth of course. So that the seeds would set right and so we'd all have a good harvest in the summer. It was good fun was Plough Monday, so don't you go saying that ploughs are boring, young lady. You wouldn't have been bored if you'd lived in my village when Plough Monday came round.' And Seth walked away.

The girl looked at her friend and her friend looked at her. Then they both listened carefully to what Malcolm was telling them about the ploughs.

In the afternoon the children had their ride on Megan's horse-bus, and on the barge pulled by Megan in all her ribbons and bobbins. They had a really good school visit and the girl who thought the ploughs were boring never forgot the story of Plough Monday.

I wonder if you'd like to take part in a Plough Monday festival? I think it sounds fun. There are hundreds of different special days each year. Some of them are celebrated in this country and some of them are celebrated hundreds of miles away. Some of them are celebrated every year and some of them are only half-remembered from a long time ago. But all of them are interesting to hear about, and all of them help us to know about our world.

Prayer
Thank you God, for special days. Help us to share special days with each

other. Help us to make even ordinary days special for someone, by being helpful and kind every day.

Amen

Hymn
'Each day different'   *Harlequin*

Biblical references to the theme *Week 2   Persistence*

'. . . He will persist until he causes justice to triumph.'

Matthew 12:20

'The seeds that fell in good soil stand for those who hear the message and retain it in a good and obedient heart, and they persist until they bear fruit.'

Luke 8:15

'Be persistent in prayer, and keep alert as you pray, giving thanks to God.'

Colossians 4:2

The certificate *Week 2 Persistence*

Is there something you do at school that you don't like doing, or that you find hard? Do you sometimes feel like trying to get out of doing it? Or giving up? I think everyone feels like that sometimes. Even grown-ups can have that feeling when they have to do something they know they're not very good at. I think the best way of overcoming feelings like that, is to keep trying, to keep persevering.

Andrew hated Tuesdays. Tuesday was swimming day and Andrew couldn't swim. On a Tuesday morning the whole class lined up ready for the baths bus, as soon as they'd taken the register. Everyone had to go. There was no way out of it. The only reason you could stay behind was if you had a letter from your mum or dad or the doctor to say you had an ear infection or something.

Andrew had tried all sorts of ways *not* to go to the baths with the class. He'd had a Tuesday tummy ache and he'd forgotten his swimming things, but nothing worked. He'd had to go.

It wasn't that he didn't like the baths – he did. He liked the sea and the pool when he went on holiday. But he was allowed to play – on holiday. When he went swimming with the class, he had to swim. He had to try to take his feet off the bottom of the pool and swim to the other side. He daren't take his feet off the bottom; and the other side was a million miles away.

Andrew hadn't minded swimming at the beginning of the year. Lots of his friends couldn't swim at the beginning of the year. But slowly they'd all gained their ten metres and then their 25 metres, and they'd all moved into the next swimming group. Some of them could swim a mile now, and three of them had gained silver and gold awards. But he still couldn't take his feet off the bottom, and now there was only him and a girl called Manda in the beginners' group.

Manda had given up trying. She just played around in the water and sometimes got into trouble. But Andrew didn't like getting into trouble. So each week he plodded his way across the shallow end of the baths, then back again. Back and forth. To and fro. Every week. He could do his arm stroke. That was no problem. And he could do the leg stroke; with one leg! The other leg he kept firmly on the bottom of the pool so that he wouldn't sink.

'Come on Andrew. You can do it. You won't sink. Take your other leg off the bottom. Just try it. It'll work, you'll see. Come on. Just try.' But Andrew couldn't do it.

One day the teacher said that they all had only two more weeks of swimming left. They'd been coming for nearly a year now, she said, and lots of people had made such a lot of progress. Andrew hung his head; he knew he hadn't made any progress at all, even though he'd tried. He knew the teacher wasn't proud of him.

The next week when they went to the baths, they had some huge plastic balls to play with. The better swimmers were playing some kind of team game, but the teacher knew that Andrew and Manda couldn't join in, so she threw them a ball to share.

'I'm having it,' shouted Manda.

'No you're not, it's to share,' said Andrew, and he hurried after it, determined to get it first.

Now it's very difficult hurrying through water. Andrew moved his arms and leg in breast stroke and aimed straight for the ball. It was several metres away from him. He stretched and grabbed. He got it.

'It's mine!' he shouted to Manda.

'Andrew!' called the teacher. Andrew stopped and turned to look at her. He thought she was going to be cross with him for grabbing the ball and not letting Manda have it.

But she wasn't angry.

'You did it,' she said. 'You did it. At least five metres. Well done. You could easily do ten. Come on. Have a go.'

Andrew looked at her, puzzled.

'You took your feet off the bottom, Andrew. Both of them. You swam. Do it again.'

Suddenly Andrew's knees felt wobbly as he realised that he *had* taken his feet off the bottom when he reached for the ball. Slowly he walked to the side of the pool. He held on to the bar. He took a deep breath, then he put both his feet against the wall and pushed away as hard as he could. He moved his arms quickly and strongly and kept his eyes on the far side of the pool. He moved both his legs just as he'd been taught to do. The other side came nearer. He had hardly any breath left. He couldn't seem to swim and breathe at the same time. He couldn't see the other side of the pool any more because of the water in his eyes. He thought he could hear a roaring sound and then suddenly he crashed, with a bump, into the far side of the pool. He put his feet on the bottom again and stood up. The roaring sound was everyone clapping and shouting. 'Well done Andrew. You did it. Well done. Ten metres.'

The next day in assembly Andrew was presented with his ten metres certificate. His teacher told everyone how hard he'd tried, how he'd not given up, how he'd persevered, and how he deserved his certificate.

Sometimes, if we persist with something, we eventually manage to do it, even though at first it seems impossible. The secret is to keep on trying.

Prayer
Dear God, if at first we don't succeed, help us to try again. Help us to be strong enough to keep going even when things seem difficult.

Amen

Hymn
'It's a new day' *Come and Praise* Vol 2

The paper birds
Week 2 Persistence

The other day I was talking to a teacher who said 'I like children who are clever, but better still, I like children who can persevere.' Do you know what she meant? She meant that she likes children who have 'stickability'; children who don't give up easily; children who keep on trying; children who stick at a thing until it's finished. I agreed with her. I think that children who can persevere deserve to do well.

Today's story is rather a sad story. It's about a small girl who was very ill. But even though she was going to die, she still perservered with something she had started to do.

Towards the end of the Second World War, a nuclear bomb was dropped on a city called Hiroshima, in Japan. The bomb killed many people, and many others became ill because of the radiation from the nuclear explosion.

Living in Hiroshima at the time was a small girl called Sadako Sasaki. She became very ill with the radiation sickness, and her mother knew she would die. But Sadako's mother didn't want her daughter to give up hope. She knew that whilst Sadako believed she could live, there was a chance that she might.

Sadako's mother was very good at origami – she could make things out of paper. She could bend and fold and tear an ordinary piece of paper and turn it into a beautiful bird, or a flower, or a person, or a boat. She decided that she would teach Sadako how to make paper birds. She sat down with her and showed her how to fold the paper, how to crease it and turn it, and how to open out the bird's wings and beak. Sadako tried. Her first paper bird didn't turn out very well, but her next one was better, and the next one better still.

'I know,' said Sadako's mother, 'Let's see if you can make one thousand paper birds.' Sadako laughed at that.

'I could never make as many as that,' she said.

'You could if you tried,' said her mother. 'Perhaps if you could make a thousand paper birds, your radiation sickness would go away, and you would be well again.'

'I'll try,' said Sadako, and she began to make another paper bird, then another and another. Soon she had made four birds, but she was too tired to make any more that day. The next day she made five paper birds, and the day after that she made another six.

Over the next few weeks Sadako made more than one hundred paper birds, and her mother threaded them all together and strung them across the room, where Sadako could see them. Every day she made more, and every day the string of paper birds grew longer and longer.

Some days Sadako felt quite strong and she was able to make several birds, but on other days she felt weak and tired and ill, and was able to make only one or two.

'Keep trying,' said her mother. 'Remember, you're trying to reach your target of one thousand birds, and then perhaps you'll be well again.

Sadako kept on trying and soon her string of birds had reached two hundred, and then three hundred; four hundred; five hundred; six hundred; seven hundred; eight hundred. But by now it was clear that the radiation sickness was not going to go away. In fact Sadako was becoming weaker and weaker every day. Her mother helped her now to make each paper bird. She still believed that Sadako might not die if somehow she could manage to make one thousand birds.

Sadako was in a lot of pain now. She struggled to finish another bird – 963. The next day she made another – 964. And that one, sadly, was the last one she ever made, because Sadako died that night.

She was a very brave girl to keep trying and to keep going, even though she wasn't able to reach her target of one thousand.

That might have been the end of the story, but some people who were building a Peace Park heard about Sadako and the thousand paper birds.

'We'll decorate the Peace Park with paper birds just like the ones Sadako made,' they said. 'It will remind people of the bravery of one small girl, and perhaps it will make people never want to have a nuclear war again.'

If you ever go to visit the Peace Park in Japan, you will see monuments festooned with colourful streamers made of hundreds and thousands of folded paper birds, and you will be able to remember the story of Sadako.

Prayer
> Birds of hope
> Made in pain;
> Made in peace,
> Peace remain.
>
> *Amen*

Hymn
'God knows me' *Come and Praise* Vol 1

Practical ideas
At the beginning of this assembly I introduced the idea of origami by showing the children how to make a paper crane. A useful book with helpful diagrams is Steve and Megumi Biddle's *Step-by-step Origami* published by Ebury Press (ISBN 085223 8124).

Three frogs
Week 2 Persistence

Being able to stick at something without giving up can be a very useful thing to be able to do. It might even save your life! One of the frogs in today's story discovered that.

Once upon a time there were three frogs who were very good friends. However, they were very different from each other.

The first frog liked fun. He wasn't hardworking – he just liked enjoying himself and having a good time. He was very popular with the other frogs, because they knew that whenever he was around, something exciting was bound to happen.

The second frog was a bit of a bully. He was big and strong and always had to be first and best whenever the frogs played games together.

The third frog was an ordinary sort of fellow. He was friendly and helpful. He was good at some things and not so good at others.

One summer day the three frogs decided to go exploring. They hopped out of their pond, across the grass and through a hole in a wall. They hopped over the road, along a path and up to a farmhouse door. Then they hopped in.

They didn't know it, but they had hopped into the farm dairy. They climbed over big round cheeses and slithered across slabs of cool butter. They pattered past huge silvery churns of fresh milk and did hops over pots of yoghurt. Then they saw the cream. It was in a huge round blue-and-white-striped basin.

Of course, they didn't know what it was.

'Look!' said the first frog, 'A swimming pool! Let's go for a swim.' And he jumped straight in.

'I'll race you to the other side,' said the second frog. He pushed the third frog in, then dived in himself and swam as fast as he could to the other side.

They played for quite a time in the cool white cream. It was different from swimming in water, and it tasted better. But it was more difficult to swim in, and they soon became tired.

'Let's get out now, and see what else we can find,' said the first frog. And he tried to climb out. But the sides of the blue-and-white-striped basin were steep and slippery. There were no footholds like there were at the edge of their pond at the side of the field. The first frog tried to climb out again. Then he said, 'Oh, this is too hard for me. It's too much like hard work. I'm tired.'

And he sank to the bottom of the blue-and-white-striped basin of cream; never to be seen again.

The second frog realised the danger they were in. He knew that if they didn't manage to climb out of the basin, they would drown. Suddenly he panicked. 'I've got to get out,' he shouted. 'You've got to help me.' And he pulled himself over to the third frog and climbed on to his back so that he could have something firm to jump from. The third frog began to sink under the weight of the second frog. He gasped for air. But just as he thought he would drown, the second frog slipped and fell off his back. The second frog sank beneath the surface of the foaming cream; never to be seen again.

The third frog knew what danger he was in. He knew there was no way out of the blue-and-white-striped basin of cream. But he also knew he was going to stay alive as long as he could.

'I've got to keep swimming,' he thought. 'I've just got to keep going. I can't give up. I must go on.' And he made himself swim round and round and round and round the blue-and-white-striped basin of cream.

It became more and more difficult to swim. The third frog thought it must be because he was tired. The cream seemed to be thicker than ever. 'I've got to keep going,' he said, over and over again. His legs were by now so tired he could hardly feel them. But he made them keep moving. Push and back. Push and back. The swirling churning cream made patterns as his legs moved through it.

Suddenly his webbed foot touched something firm and solid. He concentrated hard and pushed again. There it was again. Something solid. He swam harder than ever. He summoned up the last of his energy. And it worked. The cream was changing to butter as he churned it with his strong legs. A few more laps of the basin and there it was. A lovely lump of beautiful firm pale yellow butter, large enough to jump from.

The third frog pushed against the butter lump with his back legs and jumped clear of the edge of the blue-and-white-striped basin of cream. Then he hopped and skipped and skidded and slithered over the cool tiles of the dairy floor until he was safely out through the door, leaving behind him a trail of creamy buttery spattery froggy footprints.

He was safe.

If the third frog hadn't been able to keep going, to persist, to persevere, he would no doubt have disappeared to the bottom of the basin, never to be seen again, like the other two frogs.

Prayer
Dear God, help us to keep going even when things seem difficult. Help us not to give up too easily when things seem hard.

Amen

Hymn
'I'm planting my feet'   *Come and Praise* Vol 2

Biblical references to the theme   *Week 3   Families*

'The man who brings trouble on his family will have nothing at the end.'
                                                              Proverbs 11:29

'. . . a family divided against itself falls apart.'
                                                              Luke 11:17

The new baby   *Week 3   Families*

Everyone here belongs to a family. You have people in your family at home; you have our school family; and you all belong to the family of humankind – our world family. And there's a place in every family for everyone. But the little girl in today's story didn't think there was room for her any more, in her family. You see, something had happened to change things.

The new baby that they'd waited for for so long had arrived. Sarah had been looking forward to having a new baby brother or sister, but now that it had come, she'd changed her mind.

'I don't like him,' she told her mum. 'He's always crying and he smells funny.'

'You'll like him when you get to know him better,' her mum said. 'You don't know him very well yet because he's still so new.'

'I don't like him, and I won't like him,' said Sarah, and she stuck her tongue out at the new baby.

Sarah's mum was very patient with her. After all, she was a very little girl; she was only three, it wasn't long since she'd been a baby herself. Sarah's mum decided not to worry. 'She'll get to like him soon,' she said.

But Sarah didn't get to like him. In fact as each day went by she liked him less and less, and got more and more cross with herself, and him, and everyone else. And then, to make matters worse, three of her mum's friends came round to see the new baby. They fussed and cooed over him, and wanted to take turns at holding him. They patted him and sat him up and laid him down. They brought him presents and spoke to him in silly baby voices. 'They're stupid,' thought Sarah. 'All this fuss and bother about a silly little baby. Well I'm fed up. They don't want me any more. They're all only interested in that stupid baby. Well I'll show them. I'll leave home and then they'll be sorry.' And a great big tear rolled down her cheek. She wiped it away with her sleeve and went upstairs to get her bag.

She packed her favourite teddy bear, two chocolate biscuits, and some socks with yellow stars on, then she set off out of the house and down the path. Her face was smudgy with tears and she looked very unhappy.

'Hello, are you going out?' said her dad, who was just coming in.

Sarah burst into tears and told him how horrid everyone was, and how no-one wanted her any more, and how she wasn't going to live there any more because she was leaving home and she was never ever coming back again.

'Oh dear,' said her dad. 'That will make your mum and me and the new baby very very sad.' And her dad sat down on the front doorstep with Sarah on his knee, and he told her how pleased they were when she was born, and how proud they were of her now that she was nearly grown-up, and how much they were relying on her to help with her new baby brother.

'You see, you've got a special place in our family that's just for you – Sarah. No-one can take that away, not even the new baby. He will have a place, but that will be his; and your place is yours. There's enough room in families for everyone.'

Sarah and her dad went inside then, and he helped her to unpack her teddy bear and her socks with the yellow stars on. Then they sat side by side on her bed and ate the two chocolate biscuits.

I'm glad Sarah changed her mind about leaving home. I think she was jealous of the new baby, but I think she started to like him when she got to know him better.

Prayer
Dear God, thank you for families. Help us to know that there is room in a family for everyone. Help us to look after the people in our family at home, and the people in our family at school, and the people in our world family.

Amen

Hymn
'At half past three we go home to tea'   *Someone's singing, Lord*

14|1|02

The village church (Christian Unity Week)   *Week 3   Families*

Did you know that Christians go to different kinds of churches? Some people go to a Methodist church, some people go to a Catholic church, some go to a Reform church, some go to an Anglican church and some go to still other churches. This week (week ending 25th January) is called Christian Unity Week. This is when people from all the different Christian

Churches try to get together. They go to each others' churches, and share in activities together. They try to remember that they all belong to the same Christian family.

But in today's story, a whole villageful of people forgot that they belonged to that family, until someone made them remember.

The village was called Barcroft, and it had lots of houses, a shop, a pub, a post office, a school and three churches. One was a Methodist church. One was an Anglican church. And one was a Roman Catholic church. Nearly everyone in the village went to one of the churches, but they never ever went to each others'.

They either didn't like the songs, or they didn't like the priest, or they didn't like the building, or the prayers, or the books. They just didn't like each others' churches. In fact – they just didn't like each other.

It had been like that for years. Lots of the people had fallen out with other people in the village, and now most of them simply didn't speak to each other, unless it was to complain about something.

And then a new family moved into the village. There was Mum, Dad, Grandma, two boys, and a girl. Every Sunday they all went to church, but the funny things was, they didn't go to the same one. Mum and the two boys went to one church. Dad went to the other, and Grandma and the girl went to chapel.

'It's very odd,' someone said, 'a whole family all going to different churches.'

'Well I never know who to talk to,' said someone else. 'I usually only speak to chapel people, but I can't speak to Grandma and ignore the others in the same family, can I!'

'It's very difficult,' said someone else. 'Have you noticed that they all talk to everyone? They seem to be friendly with the whole village. I don't know what it's going to lead to; before we know where we are everyone will be friends with everyone else, and we've never had that here.'

'It's not right,' said another villager, 'for years and years we've all known exactly where we stand; church people talk to church people and chapel people talk to chapel people. That's the way it's always been.'

Soon life became even more complicated for the people of Barcroft because one night there was a fierce storm. The wind howled round the houses and the rain beat down. Everyone was asleep when it started, but no-one was still asleep by the time the storm stopped. It flew through the village tearing at trees and buildings. Branches littered the lanes, and greenhouses and garden sheds blew down. Then came the strongest gust of wind of all. The slates on the chapel roof rattled and shook and began to dance up and down. Then suddenly they all blew off as though someone had unzipped them. They flew in all directions. Some crashed in through people's windows; others landed on top of cars, and dented metal and smashed glass. Some fell to the ground and smashed to smithereens. The rain poured in to the roofless chapel and flooded the floor.

In the morning when the storm had died away, the people went to see the damage.

'Isn't it dreadful. Whatever are we going to do?' said the chapel people.

'It serves them right!' said the church people. 'If they'd mended the roof years ago when it needed it, this would never have happened.'

'Don't worry,' said the new family. 'If we all help, we can soon have everything mended again. Now, who's going to clean the floor, saw some wood, fetch some new tiles, or do another job?'

All the villagers of Barcroft looked ashamed. Not one of them would have suggested working together to put things right. But here was the new family expecting them all to help. And they all realised that there was no reason why they shouldn't all help. After all, the chapel *was* in their village, and the chapel people *were* part of their village. They were all one big family, everyone knew that.

The story doesn't actually say what happened next. What do you think? I think they all helped and they mended the roof. I hope then that they stayed friends and helped each other with other things too.

Prayer

Dear God, help us to know that people are still people no matter which church they go to, or what they believe. Help us to know that we belong to a family where we live: that our neighbours are part of our neighbourhood family. Help us to help our neighbours when we can.

Amen

Hymn

'The family of man'   *Come and Praise* Vol 1

The birthday party

Week 3   Families

I wonder what is the most important thing on your mind right now? Different things are important to different people at different times; so the most important thing to you now, probably wasn't the most important thing last week, and may not be the most important thing to you next week.

In today's story, John could think about nothing else but his birthday. It was more important to him than anything else.

It was going to be in five days' time and it would be John's ninth birthday. He just couldn't wait. He was having a new football strip, new boots and a real leather ball from his mum and dad. He was also having a party. He had thought that nine-year-olds were a bit old for birthday parties, but his friend Josh had had a birthday only last week and they'd all gone to the baths and then for a pizza. It had been great.

'Mum, can we go to the sports centre, then to MacDonalds afterwards?'

'I don't see why not,' his mum had said. So that's what they were going to do. He was having ten of his friends, and they were going to the baths and to the indoor football pitch. With a bit of luck they might see one or two of the city players. John hoped so.

The only problem was Samantha. She was John's sister and was six.

'Does she have to come?' said John. 'She'll spoil everything. She's a girl and she's a baby. She'll get in the way and all my friends will think I'm soppy if I have to take my little sister along. Can't she stay at home?'

'No. She cannot. She's your sister and the least you can do is to have her along to your birthday party. You could be generous and ask her to bring along a friend of her own!'

'Oh no! Not two six-year-olds. You can't be serious. They'll all laugh at me.'

'Then they're not friends worth having,' said his Mum. 'She's coming and that's that.'

John decided that he was not going to let Sam spoil his birthday treat. He would just ignore her and talk to his friends. Then they would understand that he'd had to bring her along and that he didn't really want to.

The day before his birthday arrived. John wished and wished that the day would go quickly so that tomorrow would come. He couldn't concentrate on his work at school and he went around reminding everyone about his party the next day. At hometime he rushed in to tell his mum not to forget to take spare trunks and towels in case any of his friends forgot theirs . . . but strangely she wasn't there. The next-door neighbour was there instead.

'Where's Mum?' asked John.

'She's had to go to the hospital,' the neighbour said. 'It's your Samantha. She's all right but she was knocked down by a car on her way home. We think she's broken her leg. Your mum's staying at the hospital tonight, so you can come and sleep at our house. You can share Tim's room.'

'What about Dad?' asked John. And just then his dad came in.

'We'll go to the hospital to see Sam, in a few minutes,' said Dad. 'Then when we come back, you'll go to Tim's house, and I'll go back to see Sam, then come home. I've to leave early for work tomorrow and I might have to drive up north, so I could be away a couple of days. You'll be all right at Tim's house though, won't you?'

'Yes Dad,' said John.

And do you know, he never once thought about his birthday, or his presents in the morning, or the party at the sports centre or MacDonalds. All John's thoughts were for Sam. After all, she'd been his sister for six years. He would miss her whilst she was in hospital. He hoped her leg wasn't very painful. He remembered how his arm had hurt when he broke it playing rounders. Poor Sam.

Later, when he was in bed at Tim's house, John remembered his birthday. A few more hours and it would be here. But suddenly it didn't seem nearly as important as it had done. What mattered now was that Sam should be well again. He'd have his birthday treats later on, when Sam was home again and feeling better: when she could join in. After all, you couldn't have your birthday party without your little sister, could you?

John discovered that the people in his family were more important to him than his birthday party. At the start of the story I thought he was rather a selfish boy, but he wasn't really, was he?

Prayer
Dear God, please help us to care for the people in our families. Help us to remember that each person in a family is different, but that they all have a place in the family.

Amen

Hymn
'Love will never come to an end' *Come and Praise* Vol 2

Biblical references to the theme
Week 4   Light

'No one lights a lamp and puts it under a bowl; instead he puts it on the lampstand, where it gives light for everyone in the house. In the same way your light must shine before people, so that they will see the good things you do and praise your Father in heaven.'

Matthew 5:15-16

'Jesus spoke to the Pharisees again. "I am the light of the world," he said. "Whoever follows me will have the light of life and will never walk in darkness." '

John 8:12

Candlemas Day (February 2nd)   *Week 4   Light*

Today is exactly 40 days after Christmas Day. It is called Candlemas Day. Christians believe that long ago, on this day, Jesus was taken by Mary and Joseph to the temple for the first time. There they were told that Jesus would be 'a light to lighten the Gentiles'. They were told that he had been chosen by God to help the world. Mary and Joseph were amazed at the things they were told: they had known that Jesus was special, but they had not realised just how special.

Nowadays, candles are lit in church on Candlemas Day, to represent Jesus as the light of the world.

Many years ago, country people used to believe that animals – especially badgers – woke up on Candlemas Day, to see if it was still winter. Here is one of their stories.

The old grandfather badger woke in his set. He felt stiff and cold and old. He sniffed the frosty air in the burrow. He was right. Candlemas Day. Time to look out. Time to decide about the next 40 days.

The last time he had looked out was 40 days ago, Christmas Eve, the time when all animals wake and perhaps talk. Then the hibernating ones went back to sleep again. 40 days of sleep, and now it was Candlemas.

He nudged the sleeping badger next to him. 'Wake up. Time to look out. Time to decide.'

The badger shuffled and snuffled. He turned over, and in so doing disturbed the one asleep on his other side. He disturbed his neighbours, who woke theirs, and soon the whole set was awake with grumbling, mumbling noise.

'What is it?'

'Is it Spring?'

'Is it time to get up?'

'I'm tired.'

'Can I go back to sleep again?'

'No!' said Grandfather badger. 'It's Candlemas. Wake up.'

'What's Candlemas?' asked one of the youngsters.

'It's the day we decide,' said Grandfather. 'Now, you young ones, listen carefully. Go above ground and look. Smell the air. Listen. Touch the grass. Taste the weather. Then come back to the set and tell me what there is to tell. Off you go. Go!'

The young badgers were not at all sure what it was they were supposed to tell. They didn't understand what it was that had to be decided. But they trusted Grandfather, so off they went, scampering above ground, out of the burrow, cautious at first, then more confident.

They ran along the hedgerow, past the big beech tree. They saw the first signs of Spring – tiny yellow coltsfoot flowers and the first blackthorn blossom.

Then they saw something else!

Dark scary shapes that followed them everywhere. First the badgers froze with fear, then they took to their heels and ran, but the dark and terrible shapes followed them. More than that, they seemed to be fastened to their feet. The badgers tried to shake the dreadful demons off their legs, but nothing they could do would move them.

In terror they ran for their lives back to the burrow, back to the safety of the set. They tumbled down down to the deepest part, to Grandfather.

'They're after us,' they cried. 'Dreadful things which stuck to our feet and wouldn't let go. Don't make us go up there again.'

Grandfather badger smiled. 'That's the answer,' he said. 'You've decided. Those demons that frightened you were nothing but your own shadows. When shadows fall it means the sun is shining. And if the sun shines on Candlemas Day, there'll be a bit more winter, so it's not time to get up yet. You can all have another 40 days of sleep before you need to get up for the Spring.'

'But what if the sun hadn't been shining?' asked one of the badgers.

'Then it would have been time to get up now,' said Grandfather. 'But it isn't, so goodnight.' And he turned over and went back to sleep.

The rest of the badgers sighed and wriggled then sank into a sleepy heap, for another 40 days.

This old legend tells us that if Candlemas Day is sunny, winter is not finished yet; but if the day is cloudy, there'll be an early Spring.

'If Candlemas Day be fair and bright
Winter will take another flight.
If Candlemas Day be cloud and rain
Winter is gone and will not come again.'

Perhaps you could watch the weather today, and predict what you think will happen.

And you might be interested to know that this legend is also known in America. But there they believe that a groundhog – not a badger – looks out on Candlemas Day. And they call the day 'Groundhog Day'.

Prayer

Thank you God, for light. Thank you for the seasons and the different light of winter, spring, summer and autumn. Thank you for all the different kinds of weather, and the different lights each one brings. Thank you for the brightness of day and the darkness of night.

Amen

Hymn
'All things bright and beautiful'   *Come and Praise* Vol 1

Two princes go to market   *Week 4   Light*

Light is a very wonderful thing. Without light, we wouldn't be able to see anything. And if we can't see something, we might think it's not even there.

Last year when I went on holiday, we arrived at our hotel in the middle of the night. I looked out of the window, but I couldn't see anything. I could hear a few trees rustling, that was all. I didn't think there was anything interesting outside the window.

In the morning, I drew back the curtains, and I could hardly believe my eyes. There in front of me was the most beautiful view I think I have ever seen. I could see steep craggy cliffs with a tiny village clinging to the side. I could see a sparkling blue sea with small boats bobbing about on it. I could see beautiful trees and flowering bushes along the pathways leading down to the sea. And all where I thought there was nothing, just because I hadn't been able to see it the night before.

So, we need light to be able to see.

Once upon a time there was a king who had two sons. The king knew that eventually the older prince would take his place as king, but he was sure that the younger boy was the wiser of the two.

He decided to set the boys a challenge.

'You are each to take a silver coin,' he said. 'You are to go to the market and buy something that would help you if you were king. Then you are to come back and show me what you have bought.'

'There's no point,' said the older boy. 'I will be king when the time is right. There is no point in my younger brother doing this task.'

'You may be older and bigger,' said the king. 'But perhaps you will learn that you may not be wiser. You may learn something from your younger brother.'

'I don't think I'll learn anything from *him*,' said the older boy.

The king gave each of the boys a silver coin and they both set off to the market. The eldest son walked past the first few stalls. Nothing here that would help him when he was king. He walked a bit further. He saw stalls selling fruit, vegetables, cakes, shoes, flowers, hats, string, rabbits, furniture, cups, saucers, paper, pens . . .

Paper and pens! That was it, he thought. If he were king he would have to make laws and rules. He would have to send messages to his ministers to tell them what to do. He would have to write everything down so that everyone understood quite clearly what he had decided.

So without any further searching or thought, the elder prince bought as much paper, and as many pencils, pens, bottles of ink, and sealing wax, as his silver coin would allow. He put all his purchases into a huge carrier bag and set off home again.

Meanwhile the younger prince was walking through the market. He too saw all the stalls of food, meat, sweets, pans, garden tools, fish, books, pots, candles, paper, paint, wheels, everything. He saw what he wanted to buy. But he didn't buy it straight away. He wanted to be sure he had chosen the right thing, so he walked round the whole market three more times looking at everything on sale.

By now he was sure he had chosen the right thing. He went to the stall and bought just one. The stallholder wrapped it in a piece of tissue paper and gave the prince his change. The prince put his change in one pocket and the small tissue paper parcel in the other. Then he went home.

'Well!' said the king. 'And what have you bought. Let's see how wise my boys are and what they've bought to help them if they are ever king.'

The eldest prince tipped out the contents of his carrier bag on to the floor.

'I've bought paper and pens,' he said. 'A king needs to order people about and make laws. A king would need to write all the rules down. I've brought paper and pens for writing down rules.'

The second son brought the little parcel out of his pocket and carefully unwrapped it. It was a candle. A small slim white candle.

'The light of this candle can fill a room,' he said. 'A candle would help me to see clearly, and a king needs to be able to see clearly to understand his people.' The younger son put his candle in a tiny holder and lit it. The flame burned brightly and its light shone out.

'You are a very wise boy,' said the king. 'Your elder brother will undoubtedly be king when I am gone, but you will be his chief advisor and his counsellor. You will help him to see clearly. You will help him to use his power with care and understanding.

'Perhaps I can learn something from my little brother, after all,' said the older prince.

Many years later the king died and the elder son became king in his place. He appointed his younger brother Chief Advisor, and together they ruled the kingdom in a fair and kind way. They both knew that they could learn from each other.

Sometimes we can all be a bit bossy with people younger than us. Often we think we're cleverer than them just because we're older. But, we can all learn something from other people, even if they are younger than us.

Prayer
Dear God, thank you for the light that helps us to see. Thank you for the light that helps us to understand. Help us to remember that we can learn from everyone, whether they are older or younger than us.

Amen

Hymn
'Flickering candles in the night'   *Come and Praise* Vol 2

The dragon and the dark   *Week 4   Light*

Have you ever been frightened of the dark? I think nearly everyone has at some time or another. The dark can seem quite scary because we can't see beyond it. We don't know what's there because it's too dark to see into. Today's story is about someone who was frightened of the dark.

Del Fuego was a dragon. He was 368 years old and was enormous. He had green spotted scales all down his back and a purple and pink underneath. He had a long nose with huge flaring nostrils, and big bright eyes like burning coals, high on his face. He breathed long shooting tongues of flame, and his roar was loud enough to crack a mountain. His talons were so strong he could tear up 20 trees at one stroke.

Del Fuego lived in a cave by the side of the sea. During the day he sat on the sand and watched the boats sail by, or sometimes he climbed to the top of the cliff to watch the cars and caravans. The days were not too bad, but the nights were dreadful. You see, Del Fuego was afraid of the dark.

At night when the daylight faded and the sky became dull and grey, Del Fuego disappeared into his cave, climbed onto his rocky shelf, and pulled his blanket up over his eyes. Then he stayed there shivering, until the morning.

He could not explain why he didn't like the dark. He thought perhaps it had something to do with the fact that he couldn't see into it. He couldn't see past it, or through it, or beyond it. The dark was like a thick curtain which came over the mouth of his cave every evening and stayed there until morning.

One night Del Fuego had just settled into his blanket when he heard a sound. It was not like any sound he had heard before. He listened again. Scrunch. Scrunch. He lay very still. SCRUNCH. SCRUNCH. The sound came nearer. Del Fuego hardly dared to breathe.

Suddenly he heard voices. He poked his head out of his blanket. Someone was there. Someone was walking across the pebbles. Del Fuego lay stiff with fright. Perhaps it was smugglers . . . or murderers . . . or burglars . . .

'Hey! Look!' said a voice. 'There's a cave over here. We could stay here until it's light.'

'Good idea,' said another voice. 'I don't want to stay out here in the dark. It's scary.'

Two men came and stood in the entrance to Del Fuego's cave. They shone torches round the inside of the cave. But they didn't see the shelf high on the wall with Del Fuego lying wrapped in his blanket. The two men sat down with their backs against the wall.

'There should be lights on these cliffs,' said one of them.

'You're right,' said the other. 'If we'd been able to see where we were going, we wouldn't have run aground with the boat. Someone should build a lighthouse. I mean, people could get killed on these rocks, there's no warning is there?'

Del Fuego listened to this conversation, and realised that the men were not smugglers or murderers or burglars, but ordinary fishermen whose boat had run aground on his beach. He decided to stay quite still on his shelf until the morning. Then the men would go away, and everything would be back to normal again.

But while he was thinking this, Del Fuego's blanket was slipping from the shelf. It slowly dipped down until one hairy corner was dangling in the fisherman's face. He jumped up and shone his torch to see what it was. The two fishermen looked straight into the eyes of Del Fuego, and he looked into theirs.

It was difficult to know who was the most scared. First they all three stayed stock still. Then they all screamed. Then they all tried to run in different directions all at the same time and ended up sitting in a tangled heap on the floor.

'I knew it would happen,' wailed Del Fuego. 'I always knew that one night something dreadful would happen in the dark. Just when it's so scary. Just when you can't see.'

'Well, I don't know why you don't do something about it,' said one of the fishermen. 'You live in this cave, you could light a beacon every night when it gets dark, then all the boats would be able to see the rocks and the cliffs. You could light up the whole beach. You could nearly turn yourself into a lighthouse – your eyes are as bright as light bulbs!'

'I never thought of that,' said Del Fuego. 'That's a good idea. I'll come out of my cave every night and I'll light up the coast with my eyes and my flame, then it won't be dark, and all the boats will be able to see.'

And that's what he did. Later, a lighthouse was built on the top of the dragon's cliff, and every night he made sure that the light was lit to protect the boats that were out at sea in the dark.

So the next time you see a lighthouse, look carefully at the base of it. There might be a dragon curled up asleep. Del Fuego sleeps during the day now, because he's too busy to sleep at night, he has too much work to do. And oddly enough, he's no longer afraid of the dark.

Del Fuego discovered that the dark was not as scary as he thought it was.

Prayer
Thank you God, for day and night. Thank you for light and darkness. Thank you for sunshine and shadows, light and shade. Help us to know that we need light and dark in our lives.

Amen

Hymn
'Father we thank you for the night'   *Someone's singing, Lord*

Practical ideas
Any primary school work on light is hardly complete without the inclusion of *The owl who was afraid of the dark*, a delightful story by Jill Tomlinson, published by Penguin Books (ISBN 0 14 030634 X).

Biblical references to the theme   *Week 5   Promises*

'People who promise things that they never give are like clouds and wind that bring no rain.'

Proverbs 25:14

'God keeps every promise he makes. He is like a shield for all who seek his protection.'

Proverbs 30:5

'Better not to promise at all than to make a promise and not keep it.'

Ecclesiastes 5:5

The Pied Piper
adapted from 'The Pied Piper of Hamelin' by Robert Browning

What do you have to do if you make a promise? Yes, everyone knows you have to try to keep it. If you don't try to keep a promise, then the promise becomes worthless, and no-one will believe you next time you promise something.

In today's story someone tried to wriggle out of a promise they had made; the story doesn't end very happily.

Once upon a time in Germany, there was a lovely town at the edge of a river. It would have been wonderful to live there – except for one thing. Rats!

They were everywhere. The town was overrun with them.

They fought the dogs and killed the cats
And bit the babies in the cradles.

The people of the town had tried every way they could think of to get rid of the rats, but nothing had worked. At last the people became so angry about the whole situation, they marched to the Town Hall and demanded that the Lord Mayor do something about it.

'We've had enough,' they shouted. 'It's time you sorted out the problem. It's your job. Get rid of the rats . . . or we'll get rid of you!'

The Lord Mayor groaned. He had no more ideas left and his head ached with trying to think. He called the councillors together so that they could have another meeting. But just as they sat down at the council table there was a tiny noise at the door.

'Come in,' said the Mayor.

The door squeaked open and a strange-looking man came into the room.

His queer long coat from heel to head
Was half of yellow and half of red;
And he himself was tall and thin
With sharp blue eyes each like a pin.

He wore a red and yellow scarf around his neck, and at the end of it dangled a pipe, like a recorder.

'Hello,' he said. 'I am the Pied Piper. I have magic in my pipe and I could whistle away your rats for you. Will you pay me a thousand pounds if I do?'

'A thousand pounds!' said the astonished Lord Mayor. 'No. I'll not pay you a thousand pounds. I promise you I'll pay fifty thousand pounds if you can rid our town of rats.'

The Pied Piper stepped into the street. He put his pipe to his lips and before the first three notes had played, there was a sound. A sound like a muttering.

And the muttering grew to a grumbling;
And the grumbling grew to a mighty rumbling;
And out of the houses the rats came tumbling.

There were big rats, small rats, thin rats, fat rats. Old rats, young rats, brown rats, black rats. All of them scurrying, hurrying, scrabbling and scrambling, following the Piper, and the magic tune.

He led them dancing through the streets of the town, round the corners, up and down, along to the river, and there he stopped. But he didn't stop playing and the rats plunged into the water, and drowned. All except one, who managed to swim across to the other side.

The Piper turned back to the town.

'May I have my fifty thousand pounds now?' he asked.

The Mayor stood still, and the council stood, as if they were turned into blocks of wood.

'Fifty thousand pounds,' said the Mayor. 'We haven't got fifty pence! We can't pay you, we've no money.'

The Piper stood quite still.

'You promised,' he said.

'A promise?' said the Lord Mayor. 'We didn't mean it. Anyway, there's nothing you can do now. The rats are gone, I saw them drown with my own eyes.'

'I'll blow my pipe again,' said the Piper, 'if you don't keep your promise.'

'Go on then,' said the Mayor. 'Blow your pipe. Blow your pipe until you burst.'

The Piper put his pipe to his lips again and played three long, sad, sweet notes. Before the last note had died away,

There was a rustling, that seemed like a bustling.
Small feet were pattering, wooden shoes clattering,
Little hands clapping, and little tongues chattering.

Out of the houses came all the boys and girls, running and shouting, laughing and singing. He led them dancing through the streets of the town, round the corners, up and down. He piped them to the very edge of the river.

The Lord Mayor and all the people of the town stood still. Horrified. They were unable to move, or shout, or stop the Piper in any way. But the Piper turned away from the river and led the children towards Koppelberg Hill. Suddenly a huge doorway opened in the hill, and the Piper and children disappeared inside. All except one boy, who couldn't keep up with the rest, and he was left behind when the door shut fast.

The Lord Mayor sent messages north, south, east and west to try to find the Piper. He offered to give the Piper all the gold and silver he wanted. But it was too late. The Piper and the children were gone; never to be seen again.

The Lord Mayor and the people were sorry that they hadn't kept their promise. 'In future,' they said, 'if we promise someone something, we'll keep our promise.'
   I hope you think carefully before you make a promise. And having made a promise, I hope you keep it.

Prayer
Dear God, help us to keep the promises that we make. Help us to be the sort of people that others can trust. Help us to know that it is important to keep our word.

Amen

Hymn
'Think, think on these things'   *Someone's singing, Lord*

Practical ideas
The language and rhythm of the original poem is wonderful, and the italicised parts of the above story are taken directly from it. I have found that older children enjoy listening to the whole poem; younger children, to the more dramatic sections of it.
   'The Pied Piper' can be found in *The Oxford Book of Story Poems* published by Oxford University Press (ISBN 0 19 276087 4).

Urashima
Week 5   Promises
adapted from Japanese literature

The Lord Mayor, in the story of the Pied Piper, wished he'd kept his promise. If he had, the children wouldn't have disappeared. In today's story, something happened because a promise wasn't kept.

Urashima was a fisherman. One day he was bringing his boat into harbour, when he saw a large turtle on the beach. The turtle was in some distress because some cruel person had turned it on its back, and now it was struggling, unsuccessfully, to right itself again. Urashima knew that if he didn't help the turtle, it would die.
   He moored his boat safely in the harbour, and then walked back to the

beach. By now the turtle was quite weak. Urashima gently turned the turtle over and led it back to the sea. It stayed at the edge of the waves for a while, and then began to swim away. Urashima was pleased.

A few days later, Urashima was far out in the bay, with his nets spread all around, when something bumped against the boat. It was the turtle. And to Urashima's surprise, it spoke. Then, to Urashima's absolute astonishment, it changed from a turtle into a beautiful sea princess.

'I am the daughter of the Dragon King of the Sea,' she said. 'Thank you for saving my life. Will you come and see my Father's kingdom, deep beneath the waves?'

'I can't come with you,' laughed Urashima. 'If I come with you deep beneath the waves, I'll drown.'

'No,' she said. 'Come.'

Urashima did as she asked and went with her to the kingdom under the sea. It was the most beautiful and wonderful place he had ever dreamed of seeing.

Urashima and the Dragon King's Sea Princess fell in love and were married; and the Dragon King was pleased to accept Urashima as his son-in-law.

After a while, Urashima wanted to see his old home again and visit his parents. He wanted to know that they were well, and he wanted to tell them of his marriage to the Sea Dragon Princess. The Princess was not happy about his wanting to visit his old life again, but she did not want to stop him from going. Urashima promised that he would not be gone long, and that he would come back to her in the kingdom under the sea. It was not a difficult promise to make because Urashima loved the Princess and liked his new life.

On the day that he was to leave for the visit, the Sea Dragon Princess gave Urashima a beautiful painted box, fastened with a silken thread.

'It is to say I love you,' she said. 'But you must make me another promise. Say that you will.'

'What do you want me to promise?' asked Urashima. 'I have already promised that I will come back to you as quickly as I can.'

'You must promise me that you will not open the painted box. You must keep it tied with its silken thread. You must not open it. If you do, you will not see me again. Promise.'

'I promise,' said Urashima. 'But I don't see what harm a little box can do.' And he laughed.

The Princess, in her turtle shape, travelled with Urashima as far as the edge of the sea, then left him to find his own way to his old home. Urashima walked along the cliffs that he knew so well, towards the town. But here, everything seemed different. The streets and the houses had changed. The people looked different and there was no-one that Urashima recognised. He couldn't find his parents' house or their street or anyone who had ever heard of them.

Urashima couldn't understand it. He began to feel worried and afraid. Then he came upon an old old man, and asked him if he knew about his parents.

The old old man looked strangely at Urashima, and then he spoke.

'They have been dead for hundreds of years,' he said. 'People say that they had a son called Urashima, but he went fishing one day and drowned in the sea. That was over four hundred years ago. Why do you ask?'

But Urashima didn't answer. He was too shocked to hear what the old man had told him. He walked away, back to the edge of the sea. He sat on the sand. Now he knew that the time he had spent in the kingdom under the sea was different from time in the human world. He wondered how it could happen, and what he should do next.

He remembered the painted box tied with thread, that the Princess had given him. He took it out of his pocket. He looked at it. He remembered his promise; but slowly he untied the silken thread and let it fall on the sand. Slowly he pushed open the lid.

The years, like a wisp of white smoke, curled out of the box and blew away in the wind and the sea-spray. And as they disappeared for all time, Urashima grew old. His hair turned white and his skin became rice-paper thin. His eyes grew cloudy and his heart stopped beating.

Later, the people of the town found his body lying at the edge of the sea. Urashima had broken his promise and would never see his Sea Dragon Princess again.

I wonder how the story would have ended if Urashima had kept his promise. Perhaps you could write a different ending! Perhaps you could say how the Princess explained the mystery of time!

Prayer
Thank you God, for stories and words. When we use words to make promises, please help us to keep those promises.

Amen

Hymn
'A living song' *Come and Praise* Vol 1

Hetain's promise

When was the last time you made a promise? Do you make a lot of promises? Some people make them all the time. They say 'I promise to be your friend', or 'I promise to be good', or 'I promise to tell the truth', or 'I promise to come and see you'. Some people make promises without really meaning what they say, and then they can make other people unhappy.

Hetain was eight and was going on holiday to see his grandma and grandad. He'd seen them before, but only once when he was about three, because they lived a long long way away from Hetain's house. Hetain's mum and dad had a shop and weren't able to take holidays very often.

Hetain was very excited about the holiday. He just couldn't wait to set off. But at last it was time to go. They travelled by train to London and then by plane to India. It was a long flight, but Hetain wouldn't let himself go to sleep – he wanted to see everything and miss nothing.

When the plane touched down at Bombay airport, his uncle was there to meet them and to take them to Hetain's grandparents' house.

At first Hetain was very shy. He could hardly remember his grandma and grandad. He'd been so very small the last time they'd met, but he soon got to know them all over again and everyone had a wonderful holiday. The time went so fast.

'Well, now that you are so grown-up, and doing so well at school, you must write letters to us,' his grandma said. 'And then we'll be able to keep up with all your news. That would make us very happy.'

'Yes, that's a good idea,' said Hetain. 'I'm good at writing. I'm always getting stars for my stories. I'll write you hundreds of letters, I promise.'

And there it was. A promise. Made just as easily as that.

All too soon it was time for the family to set off again on the long journey home.

'Now don't you forget,' said Hetain's grandma. 'You made a promise. Write me lots and lots of letters. I want you to keep in touch.'

'I promise,' said Hetain. 'I always keep my promises.'

'I hope so,' said his grandma.

Back at home, Hetain was very busy. There was school, and Cubs, football club and television. There were his friends to play with and a project about sport he wanted to finish. Chris invited him to his birthday party and Sanjit asked him to go swimming.

But deep at the back of Hetain's mind was a little niggling thought. His promise to write. 'I'll do it later. I'm too busy just now,' he said to himself.

At her house in India, Hetain's grandma looked out eagerly every morning for the postman. She was so looking forward to having a letter from her beautiful grandchild. She had so much enjoyed seeing him again after all that time. He had been such a little boy the last time she had seen him, but now he was nearly grown up. And he could write. He'd said he was good at writing, so there would be a letter from him soon. Perhaps if not today, then tomorrow. It would come soon. She knew it would because he promised.

Hetain was still very busy. He'd joined a swimming club now with Sanjit and they went with his mum after school every Tuesday. Next weekend he was going to cub camp with the pack. He was looking forward to that. Always so much to do. Always so busy. But always that small niggle-thought at the back of his mind. The letter. The promise. It was making him feel quite uncomfortable.

Hetain's grandma was very disappointed. She still looked for the postman every day. But she didn't think he would have anything for her. She was very upset. She had so looked forward to a letter with news of everything Hetain had been doing. Perhaps there would be a letter tomorrow – but she didn't really think so.

And then she had an idea. 'Perhaps the promise needs a little reminder,' she thought. She got out her paper and pen and sat down at her table.

'Dear Hetain,' she wrote. 'Hello. I know you said you would write to me, but I thought I would write to you first. I know how exciting it is to get a letter through the post, so here's one from me.' She went on to tell him all sorts of things that she and his grandad had been doing. When she finished the letter, she tucked a few coloured post-cards into the envelope, and took it to the post office to post.

A few days later it arrived at Hetain's house. His grandma was right; it was exciting getting a letter through the post. Hetain thought of his gran, waiting every day for the postman to bring a letter from him, and he knew how selfish he'd been in not keeping his promise. He went straight up to his room and chose one of the postcards from the envelope. He wrote in his best writing, 'Hi gran. I went swimming with Sanjit and I can swim ten lengths. I'm going to cub camp on Saturday. I'll write you another letter soon. Lots of love from Hetain.' He asked his mum for a stamp and went to post the card in the letter box at the end of the street.

A week later, a very happy and proud grandma was showing all her friends the postcard from Hetain.

'He's a very clever boy,' she said. 'Look how well he writes. He promised he'd write and I knew he would.'

It's very easy to make a promise, but not so easy to keep one. If Hetain hadn't kept his promise, his grandma would have been very unhappy, and I don't think Hetain would have felt good about it; do you?

Prayer

Dear God, help us to think carefully before we make a promise. Help us to know that we can make someone feel sad and unhappy if we don't keep a promise to them.

Amen

Hymn

'God has promised' *Come and Praise* Vol 1

Biblical references to the theme

Week 6 Listening

'Listen to what is wise and try to understand it.'

Proverbs 2:2

'My sheep listen to my voice; I know them and they follow me.'

John 10:27

'Everyone must be quick to listen, but slow to speak and slow to become angry.'

James 1:19

The listening tree

Week 6 Listening

Have you noticed that some people are better at listening than others? Some people are too busy making noise themselves, to listen. Let's see how well you can listen to this story; it's about a listening tree.

The huge beech tree stood at the corner, where the gardens met the field. It was old and gnarled and bent. It stood alone but was not lonely because of all the animals who sheltered in and near it. By its roots lived rabbits, moles, mice, shrews, snails and worms. On its trunk lived scurrying insects and a green woodpecker. In its branches lived sparrows, magpies, squirrels and an owl. And at the very top was a rookery; huge nests built by black, flapping rooks.

All the animals knew that it was a listening tree. If they had a problem they could sit in its shade, or up in its branches and be still and quiet and calm. They would hear the sighing of the wind and the rustling of leaves and twigs. They would hear and feel the tree living and breathing. Often – not always – the animals would hear an answer to their problem in the sounds of the beech tree.

One day two children came to stay with their grandmother. Her garden was the last one before the field began, and the listening tree was at its corner. The children were town children. They were used to noise: ice cream vans, radios, shouting children, noise in the living room, music at the supermarket, sound everywhere. Their country grandma sometimes used to say, 'Be still for a few minutes. Go and sit under the listening tree and wait for it to speak.'

The children would sit for a minute or two, but they never heard anything, they were soon bored.

'The tree doesn't speak,' they told their grandma.

The children stayed at the house for a week. They grew noisier and noisier. Their grandma grew more and more tired, and the listening tree grew angrier by the day. They were just never still. And certainly never quiet, not even for a minute. From early morning until late evening they shouted and ran, yelled and climbed. There was no peace for neighbours, grandmas, trees or animals – most of which had gone into hiding out of the way.

At the end of the week the listening tree decided that enough was enough. He waited until the children were shrieking around his trunk, then he leapt into action.

He lashed his branches in the air and roared the wind through them. He swished his leaves in the children's faces and rattled his beech nuts down on their heads. Then he whisked his branches round their waists and whirled them high up into himself, where he held them fast and tight.

The children were too frightened and astonished to do or say anything. They just sat in the branches where they'd been put.

When the tree saw them sitting still, he made his branches and twigs still and calm again. Then he whispered to all the animals to return. They rustled and scurried back to their places in the tree. The children watched, fascinated; and listened, spellbound. They heard and saw animals they had only read about. They saw squirrels and rabbits, the green woodpecker, the mice and shrews and voles. They heard the hoot of an owl and the folding of a bat's wing.

They sat for a long time and listened and watched. At last the tree let them go and helped them down. They ran inside to tell their grandma all that they had seen and heard. She listened quietly to all they had to say.

'The listening tree is very clever,' she said at last. 'He knows how important it is to hear the still small voice of calm. I'm glad you've heard it. Remember the listening tree's message, and you will be wiser and cleverer children.'

'But what message?' they asked.

'The message to listen, of course,' she said.

After their holiday the children went back to the town; until their next holiday. And although the children were often noisy, as children often are, they sometimes were quiet, and they sometimes listened. They were quite surprised at the number of things they heard.

Of course, *you* – the children in our school – know how to be quiet sometimes. I'm glad you're not as noisy as the children in the story, but I wonder what *you* would have done if the tree had suddenly whisked you up into its branches and held you there until you were quiet? You could write a story to tell me about it.

Prayer
Help us Lord, to listen. Help us sometimes to be so quiet, that we can hear the still small voice of calm.

Amen

Hymn
'A still small voice'   *Come and Praise* Vol 2

Five rabbits   *Week 6   Listening*

When you were very small perhaps your mum read you a rhyme like this one.

'Five little rabbits went down to the shore,
One fell in the water and then there were four
Four little rabbits climbed up in a tree,
One fell from a branch and then there were three.
Three little rabbits went over the track,
A train sped along; only two came back.
Two little rabbits decided to roam,
They wandered away; just one came home.
One little rabbit played all alone,
Just one. All alone. All day. On his own.'

Perhaps the rhyme wasn't exactly the same, but it would have had the same message. The mother rabbit warned her children to keep out of danger, but although they *listened* to her, they didn't *hear*, and they certainly didn't take any notice. By the end of the poem, four of the rabbits had died, all because they took no notice of what their mother had said.

The boy in this story took no notice of his mum, either.

At the end of his street was an old house. It was falling down and no-one had lived in it for a long time. Every so often workmen came to board up a few more windows, but the boarding quickly disappeared again. In the overgrown garden of the old house was a large notice that said 'Danger. Keep out. Trespassers will be prosecuted.' The boy was not sure what the notice meant, but he knew sure enough what 'Danger. Keep out' meant. His mum was always telling him.

'Leroy, don't you go near that old building. You keep away, do you hear me?'

'Yes Mum,' Leroy always said.

'That old building's dangerous. You could get trapped if you go in there, do you hear me?'

'Yes Mum,' Leroy always said.

'An old building like that, it's time they pulled it down. It's not safe to leave it like that, especially when there's children living near. Keep away, Leroy, do you hear me?'

'Yes Mum,' Leroy always said.

But Leroy never really listened, even though he heard. He and his friends used to meet at the old house, and then sometimes, especially if it was raining, they used to go inside.

One day Leroy waited at the house for his friends to turn up, but they must have been mistaken about the time they were going to meet, because they didn't turn up.

'Well. I don't care,' said Leroy to himself. 'I'll go in anyway. I've been in loads of times. I'm not scared.'

But, in fact, Leroy was quite scared. It was one thing going into the house with the others, but it was quite a different matter going into the house on your own, with no-one else there.

He squeezed through the gap in the board over the back door and went inside. It was dark and stuffy, just like it always was. The house made groaning, moaning, sighing sort of sounds. Leroy had never really noticed them before. Usually his friends were all making so much noise they couldn't hear the sounds of the house.

Then Leroy heard a creaking sound, like a piece of old rotten wood about to give way and collapse. He turned round to where he thought the sound was coming from, and was just in time to see a huge beam of wood from the ceiling crash down on to the floor. There was an enormous cloud of dust when the beam fell. Luckily it didn't fall on Leroy. But when the dust had settled down again and Leroy was able to see, he realised that the doorway, where he had crept in, was completely blocked. How was he going to get out? No-one knew where he was. He wished he had listened to his Mum when she had warned him about going to the old house.

The story ends there. I don't know what happened next. Perhaps you can decide what you think the ending was. Did Leroy stay trapped forever? Did someone rescue him? Did his Mum find out where he was? Was she cross with him?

Remember that teachers who care about you, and your family who love you, will ask you to listen to them when they are trying to tell you things to keep you safe. Make sure you listen to them; and make sure you think.

Prayer

Dear God, please help us to listen when people who care about us are trying to tell us things to keep us safe. Help us to listen to the safety warning that the police and fire brigade give us. Help us to think before we do anything, so that we never hurt ourselves or others by our actions.

Amen

Hymn

'I listen and I listen'   *Come and Praise* Vol 1

Crocodile tears   *Week 6   Listening*

The other day someone in our school was in trouble for doing something very silly, and when I asked them why they had done that particular thing, they said, 'because so-and-so told me to.' That answer didn't make me feel any less cross; in fact it made me feel even more cross with the person. I had hoped that everyone in our school could think for themselves.

I hope that when anyone (it doesn't matter who it is) tells you to do something, you will think for yourself. If they ask you to do something sensible, that's fine. But if they tell you to do something silly, you say no. Sometimes people ask you so nicely, that it's hard to say no. But you must if you think that's the right thing to do.

Once upon a time there was a very large crocodile. He lived in the waters of a great river which flowed through a forest of trees. In the trees lived a family of monkeys, and one of them was a fine fat young one, that the crocodile would just love to eat for tea. But the fine fat monkey never came within reach of the crocodile, and so he never had the chance to catch him.

'I'll have to trick him into coming near me,' said the crocodile. 'I'll pretend to be friendly to him. I'll tell him to do things that are safe. And then I'll catch him. And eat him.'

The crocodile started sunbathing near the very edge of the river, in the shallowest places, where the fine fat monkey could see him. He didn't eat anything, or catch anything, he just lay there, still and quiet, so that the monkey could get used to him.

After a few days of doing that, he started yawning very loudly every time he saw the monkey, 'Ohhh, I'm so tired,' he said, 'I'm so tired I can't move.' The monkey became quite interested in this noisy crocodile, who lazily lay about all day, and yawned. He began sitting in a nearby tree to watch the crocodile. The crocodile watched the monkey.

'I'm a very lonely crocodile,' said the crocodile one day. 'Will you be my friend and talk to me?'

'I'm not supposed to talk to strangers,' said the monkey.

'But I'm not a stranger,' said the crocodile. 'I live here in this river and you see me every day. How can I be a stranger? You know who I am.'

The monkey said yes, he did know who the crocodile was.

'And I only want to be your friend,' went on the crocodile. 'There's no harm in that, is there?'

The monkey said, no, there was no harm in that.

'There you are then,' said the crocodile. 'We are friends. Now, come down here and talk to me. I'm not going to eat you, you know,' and he laughed as though he had just made a joke.

The monkey came a little further down the tree.

'I've got a beautiful silver pebble here under the water,' said the crocodile, 'Would you like to see it?'

'No thank you,' said the monkey.

'Well would you like to share my apple?' said the crocodile. 'I've got a lovely, juicy, ripe, round one, hidden in the grass just here.'

'No thank you,' said the monkey.

'Well what about coming to sit with me, right here at the edge of the water? Surely you'll do that, and then we can be friends.'

'No thank you,' said the monkey again, and he stayed where he was.

By now the crocodile was beginning to feel cross, because the monkey was not taken in by his friendly words. He decided to try again.

'Come down to the river,' he said. 'Come and have a drink of this cool water. I am being your friend, and asking you to share the river with me. Don't be ungrateful.'

'No thank you,' said the monkey, and he stayed in his tree.

The crocodile realised that the young monkey had been taught to say 'no' to strangers. He realised he would have to be even more cunning.

'Oh dear,' he said, 'And I did want to be your friend.' He squeezed a big crocodile tear out of the corner of his eye. 'I only wanted to be your friend,' and he squeezed another tear, and another and another. All the time, in between his tears, he kept a watchful eye on the monkey to see what he would do.

The monkey felt upset. Perhaps the crocodile hadn't meant him any harm. Perhaps he really did want to be his friend.

The monkey came a little further down the tree. The crocodile cried some more tears. The monkey climbed to the ground and started to walk towards the crocodile. The crocodile made a loud sobbing noise. The monkey stretched out his paw to pat the crocodile and make him feel better.

Snap!

The crocodile opened and shut his huge mouth in one quick movement, and the monkey disappeared.

The crocodile smiled.

Be careful when people speak to you. Listen, but think for yourself, and do what *you* think is right. Remember that the crocodile wrapped up his wicked idea in soft gentle words, and by doing that he tricked the monkey.

Prayer
Dear God, help us to think when we listen. Help us to decide in our own minds what to do, when people tell us to do things.

Amen

Hymn
'Hands to work and feet to run'   *Someone's singing, Lord*

Biblical references to the theme   *Week 7   Food*

'Share your food with the hungry and open your homes to the homeless poor. Give clothes to those who have nothing to wear, and do not refuse to help your own relatives.'

Isaiah 58:7

'After spending forty days and nights without food, Jesus was hungry.'

Matthew 4:2

The feeding of the five thousand.   Matthew 14:13-21
Mark 6:30-44
Luke 9:10-17
John 6:1-14

Pancake Day   *Week 7   Food*

Do you know Pancake Day's real name? It's called Shrove Tuesday, and it is the day before the start of Lent. During Lent, Christians remember that Jesus went into the wilderness for 40 days and 40 nights. They remember that Jesus had no food and no comfortable place to sleep. He had stones for his pillow and earth for his bed.

During Lent many Christians try to give up something they enjoy, to help them remember the difficult time that Jesus had in the desert. They use up all the rich food in their kitchen on Shrove Tuesday; they use up their eggs and butter, flour and milk. They make pancakes. In some countries the people have a carnival on Shrove Tuesday, so that they can have fun before the serious time of Lent starts. The word carnival comes from Latin, and it means to put meat aside.

But in our country, Shrove Tuesday is known as Pancake Day and I think lots of you will be having pancakes for your tea.

When I was little we used to say a rhyme about pancakes:
'Mix a pancake, stir a pancake,
Pop it in the pan,
Fry a pancake, toss a pancake,
Catch it if you can.'
I wonder how many of you could toss and catch a pancake? Some children in today's story tried.

One day Mr Foster said, 'I'll make the tea today. Who wants to help?'

'I'm busy. I'll come when I've finished reading the paper,' said Mrs Foster.

'No thanks,' said John. 'I'm reading a book.'

'I'm finishing my Lego building,' said Jane. 'I can't come.'

'Well, what would you like for tea?' asked Mr Foster.

'Sardines on toast,' said Mrs Foster.

'Spaghetti on toast,' said Jane.

'Beans on toast,' said John.

'No!' said Mr Foster. 'I think we'll have something different today. Who's coming to help?'

But again they all said no, because they were too busy doing something else.

So Mr Foster started to work in the kitchen on his own. He got out a frying pan and a mixing bowl. He got out some eggs, butter, milk and flour. 'Will someone help me mix this?' he called.

'No!' they all shouted. 'We're busy.'

Mr Foster put the frying pan on the cooker and sizzled some butter in it.

He mixed the other ingredients together in the mixing bowl. 'Will someone help me cook this?' he called.

'No!' they all shouted. 'We're busy.'

Mr Foster poured a little of the mixture into the sizzling pan. It sputtered and fizzled. Then it started to bubble and set into a golden yellow pancake. Mr Foster carried the pan to the door of the kitchen. He leaned against the door as if he didn't care whether the others watched him or not. Then quickly and skilfully, deftly and cleverly, he flipped the pancake high in the air and caught it again in the pan.

'Hey! Look at that,' said John.

'Dad!' said Jane. 'I didn't know you could do that.'

'Well I never!' said Mrs Foster. 'Fancy you being able to toss a pancake like a chef!'

'Can we have a go, Dad?' said the children.

'Well, I don't know about that,' smiled Mr Foster. 'You said you were too busy to help. You said you didn't want to help get the tea ready. You all said no!'

The story ends there, so we don't know whether Mr Foster let the others help with the pancakes or not. What do you think? I think he probably did let them help, and I think they probably had a lot of fun making the tea that afternoon. But it's a pity they didn't want to help at first.

Prayer

Dear God, please help us to do our share of helping at home and at school. Please help us to be willing to help all the time, and not just when there's something interesting and exciting to do.

Amen

Hymn
'Mix a pancake'   *Harlequin*

The feeding of the five thousand   *Week 7   Food*

Do you like going on picnics? One of the things I like best about picnics is special picnic food. I've brought my picnic basket to show you this morning. It's just an ordinary shopping basket, but I bought one the right size to fit my thermos flask and plastic sandwich boxes. Then I made a cloth cover to fit over the top of the handle and to keep everything inside clean.

I've brought some picnic food to show you. Perhaps you have food like this when you go to a picnic. You need food that's easy to eat with your fingers, don't you? I wonder how many people this picnic was made for? How many do you think? Today's story is from the Bible, it's about a small boy's picnic.

One day Jesus and his disciples set off in a boat for a quiet place where they could be alone to think and rest. But many people saw them setting off and wanted to go with them so that they could hear Jesus speak. The people set off from their towns and villages, gathering more people as they went. They arrived at the place before Jesus, and when he arrived and climbed out of his boat, there was a crowd of more than five thousand people waiting for him.

Jesus was not angry with them, even though he had wanted to be alone with his disciples. He welcomed the people and spent the whole of the day talking to them about God. When evening came, some of the disciples went to Jesus and said, 'It's getting very late. These people have had nothing to eat all day. They must be very hungry and tired. Why don't we send them away to the nearby villages, to get something to eat?'

But Jesus said 'Can't you yourselves give them something to eat?'

'We haven't any food,' said the disciples, 'And it would cost more than the wages of 200 men to go and buy even a bit of food for all these people.'

'Well, how much food have people brought with them?' asked Jesus. 'Go and see.'

So the disciples went into the crowd and asked if any of the people had brought food with them. No-one had; except one small boy, who had brought a small picnic with him.

The disciples took the boy and his picnic back to Jesus.

'There's this,' they said. 'But it isn't very much. Look, there are five small loaves and two tiny fishes. It's not enough to feed five thousand people,' they said.

'Ask the people to sit on the grass,' said Jesus.

When all the crowd was sitting down, Jesus took the bread and the fishes and said thank you to God. Then he broke the loaves and gave them to his disciples saying, 'Share this out amongst the people.' Then Jesus did the same with the fishes.

'Share this out as well,' he said.

The disciples began to share out the food among the people. The more they gave away, the more food there seemed to be. Everyone had something to eat and everyone had enough. There was even food left over that no-one could eat because everyone was full.

'Collect all the food that's left over,' said Jesus. 'So that none is wasted.'

The disciples did as Jesus asked. When they had gathered up all the crumbs, they were astonished to find that there were 12 baskets of left-overs.

Five small barley loaves and two tiny fishes had fed five thousand peoples with food left over to spare.

'Jesus is a very special person,' the people said. But Jesus went away into the hills, to be by himself.

The boy in the story probably thought his small picnic wouldn't be very much use when there were so many people to feed. But sometimes, if everyone gives a little, it turns out to be a lot in the end.

Prayer
Dear God, please help us to know that a little goes a long way when people share and trust. Help us to share what we have, and to trust in you.

Amen

Hymn
'Magic penny'   *Alleluya*

The story of cornflakes   *Week 7   Food*

What did you have for breakfast this morning? Perhaps you had an egg, or some toast, or some porridge, or perhaps you had cornflakes like me. Foods like cornflakes are so ordinary to us, that we hardly every think about them. Yet, it's not so very long ago that the first cornflake was invented; and it happened almost by accident.

When John Harvey Kellogg was a small boy, he had hot pancakes and treacle for his breakfast every day. His mum made sure that everyone in the family had a good breakfast, because they all had to work hard, even the smallest children. There were a lot of children in John Harvey Kellogg's family – 16 of them altogether, including himself. The family lived in America, over one hundred years ago, and life was tough and not much fun.

John Harvey worked hard, and when he grew up he became a doctor and went to work in a hospital. Dr John had very strong views about what people should eat if they were to be healthy. He tried to eat healthy foods himself, and now always had seven crackers and two apples for his breakfast.

Dr John became so busy at the hospital that he asked one of his brothers to help him. The brother he asked was called Will Keith. The two of them experimented with different foods that Dr John believed were healthy. They discovered how to make peanut butter, and Dr John decided he would try to make a new kind of bread to put it on.

'Boil some wheat in a big pan,' he said to Will Keith. 'And when it's cooked we'll roll it through the rolling machine and see if we can make flat bread like a pancake.'

Will Keith did as Dr John had asked. He wasn't pleased to be ordered around like this. He felt that Dr John treated him like a servant most of the time. In fact, the two brothers didn't get on at all well together and often argued.

Soon, the wheat in the pan had boiled.

'Now put it in the rolling machine,' ordered Dr John.

Again, Will Keith did as he was told. He started the machine and Dr John watched to see what would come out at the other side of the rollers. But nothing came out. Nothing that is except a wet, gluey, sticky, soggy, squashy mixture that stuck to the rollers and to every other bit of the rolling machine as well.

'Well! That didn't work, did it?' asked Dr John. 'Never mind! Clean the machine!' and he walked away to do something else.

Will Keith started to clean the rolling machine. He scraped the sticky mixture off the rollers and put it into a barrel, then he washed the machine. He was just going to throw the barrel-ful of wheat mixture away, when Dr John ordered him to go and do another job. The barrel of wheat mixture was forgotten.

It stayed just exactly where it had been left, for more than a week. And then another day. And then another. The mixture started to go mouldy and bad. It started to smell. Two more days went by. And then Dr John noticed it.

'Hey! Here's that wheat mixture that we tried to roll. Let's roll it again now, and see what happens.'

They put the mixture into the machine and were astonished to see lovely big thin flakes coming out of the rollers. Each grain of wheat was making one flake.

'Just look at that,' said Dr John. 'Let's cook them and see what happens next.'

They put some of the thin flakes into the oven and left them for a few minutes. When they took them out again the flakes were dry and crisp and golden.

'But we can't make flakes out of mouldy wheat, for people to eat,' said Will Keith. 'We might poison someone.'

'I know,' said Dr John. 'We have to find out how long we can leave the mixture so that it makes flakes when it's rolled, but not so long that it turns mouldy.

The two brothers did some more experiments and soon found out exactly how to make perfect cornflakes every time. And then, just when they'd worked out how to do it, they had another argument. Will Keith wanted to sell their new food invention and Dr John didn't want to. In the end Will Keith left the hospital, paid Dr John some money for his share in the cornflake invention, and set up a factory called the Toasted Cornflake Factory.

The Cornflake Company did very well, and lots of people liked the new breakfast food. But soon, other factories started to make cornflakes as well. Will Keith was angry about this and said that his original cornflakes were the best. He designed a new box and had 'W.K. Kellogg' written on it, so that people wouldn't confuse his original cornflakes with those made by other factories.

While the cornflake company was making cornflakes, Will Keith experimented with other cereals. Soon he had invented Rice Crispies and All Bran as well, and his factory started to make those. In a little while Will Keith Kellogg was a millionaire. Then he started to give his money away. He wanted to help people who were not as lucky as him. He gave money to needy children, to schools and hospitals, and to research centres.

And all because of a barrel-ful of mouldy old boiled wheat!

The next time you have Cornflakes, or Rice Crispies or All Bran or peanut butter, you'll be able to remember the story of John Harvey and Will Keith Kellogg.

Prayer

Dear God, thank you for all our food. Thank you for all the people who are involved in its manufacture. Thank you for all the different kinds of food we have. Help us to know that our world needs to share the food, so that everyone can have enough to eat.

Amen

Hymn

'Thank you, Lord' *Come and Praise* Vol 1

Biblical references to the theme   *Week 8   Common sense*

'Are you foolish? Learn to have sense.'

Proverbs 8:5

'Sensible people watch their step.'

Proverbs 14:15

'It does a fool no good to spend money on an education, because he has no common sense.'

Proverbs 17:16

'Truth, wisdom, learning and good sense – these are worth paying for, but too valuable for you to sell.'

Proverbs 23:23

The stupid monkeys
adapted from the Ārāmadūsaka-Jātaka

Week 8   Common sense

There are lots of different kinds of people in the world. Some of them are clever at maths, some are good at painting, others are excellent gymnasts, some are good fun to be with and make us feel happy. Everyone in the world is good at something. But not everyone has a lot of common sense! I believe that it's important to have common sense; perhaps it's more important than being clever at something.

Today's story is about someone who didn't show any common sense at all.

Once upon a time a great festival was held in the kingdom, and all the people were given a holiday so that they and their families could go out and enjoy themselves. All the people that is, except the king's gardener. He couldn't have a holiday; he had to stay in the garden and get on with his work.

You see, the king had just planted a new garden full of trees, and these trees had to be watered carefully every day so that they didn't dry and wither and die.

'I wish I could have a holiday and join in the festival,' said the gardener to himself. 'It isn't fair that I have to stay behind and work, when everyone else is out enjoying themselves. I wish I could leave the garden for the day, but if I do the trees might die, and then I would be in trouble.'

Just then he noticed a group of monkeys playing in the orchard nearby; and the gardener had an idea.

'Will you help me?' he said to the monkeys. 'Since you're in the garden anyway, will you water these new trees for me, so that I can have a day off and go and join in the festival?'

'Yes,' said the monkeys. 'We don't mind doing that for you.'

'Good,' said the gardener. 'Here's the watering can.' He gave the monkeys the can, waved goodbye, and hurried away to join all the other people at the festival.

'Right,' said the chief monkey. 'Let's get on with the job, but we must be careful not to waste any of the water. We all know that water is precious and mustn't be wasted.'

'How will we know how much water to give to each tree?' asked one of the smaller monkeys. Everyone looked puzzled. They didn't know the answer to that question. They all looked to the leader for help.

'I know,' he said, 'we'll dig up all the trees, pull them out of the ground, and look at their roots. The trees that have big roots can have a lot of water, and the trees that have little roots can have a small amount of water. That way we'll know that we've given each tree the right amount.'

The monkeys all began to chatter excitedly together.

'That's right. It's a good idea. It's the best thing to do. What a clever leader. Come on. Let's get started straight away.'

And so all the monkeys began to dig at the earth round the base of each tree. Soon they had pulled all the new trees out of the ground and they laid them down on the earth so that they could see how big each tree's roots were. Then they went away to get the water.

But, of course, the hot sun shone down on the exposed tree roots, and the roots began to wither and the trees began to die.

A wise man came walking through the garden and saw the monkeys coming back with some water. He saw the trees lying on the ground with all their roots showing.

'Whatever are you doing?' he asked.

'We're watering the trees,' the monkeys said. 'We pulled them up so that we could see how big their roots were and decide how much water to give them.'

'Oh dear!' sighed the man. 'It's a pity you didn't think and use some common sense before you started. Just look at the trees now.'

The monkeys looked. They saw the trees with their roots exposed to the hot sun. They saw the curled up, withered leaves that had been fresh and green a few minutes ago. They saw the twigs and branches dried up and brittle. They saw the blossom shrivelled and brown. They saw that they had killed the trees.

'You see,' said the wise man. 'People who try to do good can actually do harm, if they don't use common sense.'

I wonder what the gardener said when he came back? Do you think he should have made sure the monkeys could do the job properly, before he left them to get on with it? And I wonder what the king said when he found out!

I hope that you will use your common sense if anyone asks you to do a job today, and every day.

Prayer

Help us Lord, to use our common sense when we are asked to do something. Help us to think before we do anything. Help us to make sure that what we do does not hurt or harm anyone else.

Amen

Hymn

'Water of life' *Come and Praise* Vol 1

The problem field

Week 8 Common sense

I often hear the teachers in our school telling people to use their common sense. They mean that they want you to think. They want you to think before you do anything, so that you know that what you are doing is sensible. People who don't think either make silly mistakes, or do nothing at all, like the people in today's story.

Once upon a time a wise man met a number of people all arguing about a field near their houses. Let me explain. Each person had a house, and each house had a wall or a fence or a garden that touched the edge of the field. Each person thought the field ought to be theirs, because it was next to their wall or fence or garden, and each person thought that the other people had no right to the field.

The wise man said, 'Use your common sense. Think about it. The field belongs to all of you, because all your houses touch it. Common sense for a common field.' And he smiled.

The people didn't understand him. 'It can't belong to all of us. It's mine,' said one man. 'No, it's mine,' said another, and the argument started all over again. The field, by now was as muddy as a quagmire, with so much trampling about.

'Listen to me,' said the wise man. 'Look at your hand.' They all held up a hand in front of their face. 'What do you see?' he asked. The people looked at him as though he were mad. 'We see our hands!' they said.

'You see a collection of fingers,' he said. 'Five fingers that cannot do very much on their own. Can you paint a door with just your thumb? Can you cook a meal with your little finger? Can you build a rabbit hutch using just your middle finger? No. You can do all those things if you use your fingers together, but you can't do very much using only one on its own. But, when they all work together there's no end to the things they can do. People are like fingers. You can't do a great deal alone, but if you work together in a common-sense way you can achieve almost anything. Goodbye.' And the wise man walked away.

A year later he walked back again; just to see what he could see. And what do you think he saw?

He didn't see a field. He saw a beautiful park set with lawns and gardens. He saw trees and flowers. He saw swings and roundabouts for the children to play on, and seats and benches for the grown-ups to sit on and talk. He saw lots of people enjoying the park that they had made together. He saw that the people had used their common sense and had thought about the best way to sort out the problem of the field.

Things usually work best when people think sensibly and work together. I'd like to think that we have a whole school full of people who use their common sense.

Prayer
Dear God, help us to think sensibly. Help us to think when there is a problem. Help us to use our common sense and not do silly or dangerous things.

Amen

Hymn
'It's a new day'   *Come and Praise* Vol 2

The lion and the hare   *Week 8   Common sense*
adapted from the Panchatantra and from Nigerian legend

Many people say that to have common sense, and the ability to think, is the best thing in the world. I think I would agree with that. There is a story told in India and parts of Africa, which says that small animals can overcome even big powerful animals, providing they use their brains and *think*.

A large lion, the king of the beasts, had come to live in a part of the land where many other animals lived. That is precisely why the lion had chosen to live there; he had a ready-made supply of dinners, just waiting for him to eat! But the lion ate so many animals that the ones who were left began to worry.

'We shall soon be extinct if he goes on like this,' they said. 'We'll have to do something.'

The animals had a meeting and decided that they would send one animal to the lion for his dinner each day. This was less than he was eating at the moment, but if the animal was taken to the lion, he wouldn't have the trouble of having to go out and catch it each day, so he wouldn't be using as much energy and he wouldn't be needing as much food.

The animals then drew lots to decide which animals would be the lion's dinner on which days. First it was the gazelle. She was taken by the other animals to the lion's den. He ate her greedily. The next day, it was the turn of the antelope. He was eaten for dinner. Then the hyena was eaten, followed by the rabbit, and then the small monkey.

The day after the monkey was eaten by the lion, it was the turn of the hare. Now, the hare had a brain. The hare could think. The hare had a plan. The hare said, 'I'm not going to be the lion's dinner.'

'You have no choice,' said the other animals. 'It's your turn.'

'I'll go on my own,' said the hare. 'You don't need to take me. I'll go by myself.' And he went, and took his clever thoughts with him.

But he didn't go directly to the lion's den. He went to a tree nearby. He climbed the tree and waited. He waited all day. By late afternoon the lion was hungry. He came out of his den and went roaring around the forest, looking for his dinner.

'Where's my food,' he shouted. 'It should be here by now. I'm used to having my dinner delivered. Where is it?'

'I'm up here,' called the hare. 'But I can't come and be your dinner. I'm sorry, but I met the other lion who lives nearby, and he wants me to be his dinner instead. He's very fierce and strong. I didn't dare say no to him.'

'What other lion?' demanded the lion.

'The one who's just moved in to this part of the world. Didn't you know about him?'

'No,' roared the lion. 'I don't want another lion living in my territory. Show me where he is.'

'Come this way,' said the hare, and he climbed down from the tree and led the lion to a deep well, full of clear water, at the edge of the forest. 'Look down there,' he said. 'He's in there, can you see him?'

The lion leaned over the edge of the well and looked down angrily. Sure enough, looking back at him with a cross expression, was a second lion. The first lion jumped back a little; the second one did the same. The first lion edged forward carefully again; the second lion copied him. The first lion let out a mighty roar, and a huge reverberating echo danced back at him from the walls of the well.

The lion didn't think. The lion didn't wait to ask himself why a second lion should be down a well at the edge of a forest. The lion didn't question, or use his common sense. He didn't use his brain, or think what he knew about reflections. Oh no. He didn't do any of those things. He simply jumped into the well with a great yell.

'I'll . . . get . . . you . . .'
'You . . . ou . . . ou . . . ou,' called back the echo.

And the hare ran all the way back to tell the rest of the animals that he had not been eaten for dinner, and that the lion wouldn't be wanting dinner the next day, or the next day, or even the day after that.

The hare is a very small animal compared with a lion. It is not a king of animals like a lion. But it's no use having the power of a king, if you haven't any common sense to go with it. Remember, you don't have to be big and strong to be able to think. But being able to think is a very useful thing to be able to do.

Prayer
Help us God, to use our thoughts wisely. Help us to know that it is not necessary to be big and strong to be powerful. Help us to think clearly in all we do.

Amen

Hymn
'This is the day'   *Alleluya*

Biblical references to the theme   *Week 9   Neighbours*

'Don't plan anything that will hurt your neighbour; he lives beside you, trusting you.'

Proverbs 3:29

'The second most important commandment is like it: "Love your neighbour as you love yourself." '

Matthew 22:39

'But the teacher of the Law wanted to justify himself, so he asked Jesus, "Who is my neighbour?" '

Luke 10:29

A man and his neighbour   *Week 9   Neighbours*
adapted from the Panchatantra

If I say the word 'neighbours' to you, I wonder what's the first thing you think of? Perhaps you think of a programme on television; or perhaps you think of the person who's sitting next to you now. Or maybe you think of the family who lives next door to you at home.

Do you think you should be helpful and friendly to your neighbours? Today's story is about someone who tried to trick his neighbour, but the trick didn't quite work!

Once upon a time a man set off to go travelling. He locked up his house and put the key in his pocket. Then he remembered that he had left a valuable set of iron scales in the house, and he was afraid that the house might be burgled whilst he was away, and that the antique set of scales might be stolen.

'I don't know what to do,' he said to himself. 'I can't take them with me, they're far too heavy.'

Just then his neighbour came by.

'Are you off, then?' he asked.

The man explained about the valuable pair of scales, and said he didn't know what to do.

'No problem!' said the neighbour. 'I'll look after them for you. They'll be safe with me. I'm your neighbour. You can trust me.'

'That's very kind of you,' said the man. 'Thank you. Here's the key to my house. I'll be gone about a month. Goodbye.' And he set off on his travels.

Sure enough, after about a month the man returned and went to see his neighbour.

'I'm back again,' he said. 'Are my scales all right? I hope it wasn't any trouble to you to look after them for me.'

'No,' said the neighbour. 'It was no trouble, but I'm afraid there's a bit of a problem! The mice got into your house whilst you were away, and they've eaten the set of scales. I'm sorry, but there was nothing I could do about it.'

'Mice!' said the man. 'Eaten a pair of iron scales? Mice don't eat metal! What have you done to my scales?'

'Nothing,' said the neighbour. But the man knew he was not telling the truth because everyone knows that mice don't eat metal. The man believed that his neighbour had stolen the scales.

The man decided not to let the neighbour know how cross and upset he was about the loss of the scales.

'Oh well,' he said. 'Never mind. I suppose the iron tasted quite sweet to the mice. I suppose it was soft and chewy and that they enjoyed eating it.'

The neighbour was so relieved that his plan to steal the iron scales had worked, and that the man believed the story about the mice, and that he was not angry about the scales, that he offered the man a meal in his house.

'Thank you,' said the man. 'I'd like to come and eat with you, but I must go home first and have a bath. I won't be long.' He set off to his house and had just gone in through the front door, when his neighbour's son came running after him.

'My dad's sent you some of his best scented soap and a fresh clean towel,' said the boy.

'Thank you,' said the man. 'And now I want you to do something else for me. I want you to go to your friend's house, and hide there, and wait until I tell you to come out again. It's just a joke I'm playing on your dad. He won't mind. Off you go.'

The boy thought it would be fun to help with a joke, so he did as the man said and went to his friend's house to hide. The man had his bath, then went round to his neighbour's house for dinner.

'Did my boy arrive?' asked the neighbour, as soon as the man came to the door. 'I sent him round to your house with some soap and a towel, but he's been gone ages. Where is he?'

'Oh, there's a bit of a problem,' said the man. 'Your boy was on his way back to you, but a brown bird swooped down from the sky and flew off with him. I don't suppose you'll see your son again. Never mind. Is my dinner ready please?'

'What!' roared the neighbour. 'A bird. Flown off with my son? What rubbish! What have you done with him? Where is he?'

'I've told you,' said the man. 'A bird has flown off with him.'

'Birds don't fly off with grown boys!' said the neighbour.

'And mice don't eat metal!' said the man. 'Now, shall we both tell the truth?'

They did. The neighbour gave the man back his iron scales, and the man called the neighbour's boy in from his friend's house. The neighbour said he was very sorry for having tried to steal the valuable scales, and that he wouldn't ever do anything like that again. The man forgave him.

I wonder if the man and his neighbour stayed friends. I think they probably did, because the story tells us that the man forgave his neighbour for trying to trick him. I hope you never try to trick your neighbour out of something that is theirs.

Prayer
Thank you God, for friends and neighbours. Help us to try to *be* good neighbours. Help us to be kind to all our neighbours and never to do anything to hurt them.

Amen

Hymn
'Think, think on these things' *Someone's singing, Lord*

The good Samaritan
adapted from the Bible

One of the most famous stories in the world about neighbours, is in the Bible. Someone once said to Jesus, 'Who is my neighbour?' Jesus didn't give a direct answer, but instead he told the people this story.

There was once a man travelling by himself, along the road from Jerusalem to a city called Jericho. Some way along the road, the man was suddenly frightened by a group of men who rushed down the hillside towards him. They pushed him over, kicked him and punched him until he was nearly dead, then stole his money and belongings. Then they ran away. The man was so badly injured that he couldn't stand up or do anything to help himself. He just lay at the edge of the road, in a great deal of pain. There was no-one near to help him. The road was deserted. It was no use shouting for help, no-one would hear. In any case, the man was almost too weak to call for help, even if someone had been near. The best he could do was to wait for someone to come along the road who might be able to help him.

After a while, the man heard footsteps and lifted his head up a little. He saw a priest walking along towards him. A priest, thought the man, he will be a good man and he will surely help me. But the priest was busy and was hurrying towards Jericho. He saw the injured man lying at the edge of the road. He hesitated. Perhaps he should help. The man looked hurt. But no, if he stopped to help the man he would be late, and he was late enough already. He would pretend not to see him, and then no-one would know anything about it.

So the priest walked over to the other side of the road. He turned his head away so that he couldn't see the man lying at the edge of the road. He walked quickly by, on his busy hurried way.

The injured man had no strength to call out now. He laid his head down again on the dirt of the road.

A little later, more footsteps came along the road. But the man didn't hear them. He was too weak even to listen, let alone lift his head. The footsteps belonged to a Levite – a man from the same part of the country as the injured man. Perhaps he would help. After all, he was a sort of neighbour, coming from the same part of the country.

The Levite walked over to the injured man. He stopped to look at him.

He noticed how pale and ill the man looked. He wondered whether he ought to do something to help. But no, if he got involved he might get into all sorts of trouble. After all, he knew nothing about this man, he might have been in a fight that was all his fault. The men he'd been fighting with might look for the Levite and attack him. No, best leave well alone. Why should he get involved! The Levite quickly hurried away.

The injured man lay perfectly still. He was hardly breathing now. He was very weak.

After a long time another man came by. This man was a Samaritan. He couldn't be expected to help because the Samaritans were supposed to be the enemies of the country where the injured man came from. No, he couldn't help. He would walk quickly by and pretend not to see.

But the Samaritan did not walk quickly by. He stopped and bent down next to the man. 'Oh you poor man,' he said. 'Whatever happened to you? It looks as though you were attacked. Don't worry. I'll help you. I'll soon have you feeling better again.' And he went to his donkey's saddle bags and took out a bottle of water and a soft cloth. He bathed the man's wounds and gave him a drink. He helped him up on to the donkey's back and took him to the nearest village.

'This man's been hurt,' he said to the innkeeper. 'Will you look after him for me? Here's some money to pay for him. I'm travelling back this way in a few days' time. If you need any more money, I'll pay you then. Take good care of him won't you.' And the Samaritan left the injured man in the care of the innkeeper, knowing that he would be well looked after.

When Jesus had finished telling the people that story, he said to them 'Who do you think was the injured man's neighbour?' What do you think they said? Yes, they thought the Samaritan behaved like a neighbour to the man. Jesus then told the people to be like the Samaritan, and help anyone who needs help.

Prayer
Dear God, please help us to be like the Samaritan and help anyone who needs help. Help us to remember that we can be kind and helpful to each other in quite small ways; we don't have to rescue someone who's hurt, to be a good neighbour.

Amen

Hymn
'I was lying in the roadway'   *Come and Praise* Vol 2

Comic Relief Day

You may have noticed lots of red noses today! On my way to school this morning I saw people, and even cars, wearing red noses. I saw people standing at bus stops in fancy dress, and I saw people walking and driving to work in funny costumes. I saw lots of people going to school in clothes that are certainly not school uniform. Do you know why? It's red nose day; sometimes called Comic Relief Day; and it all started with a film producer, a few years ago.

He went to Africa to make plans for making a television documentary. He wanted to make a film about the people and wildlife and countryside of Africa, to show to people back home in England. He went alone first of all, to make his plans. Then he was going to bring the TV crew out to make the film.

He had arranged to have a guide who was to show him round lots of different villages, and take him to meet lots of different people.

They were travelling to a small village when they had the accident.

Luckily it wasn't a very bad accident. The truck they were driving bounced into a deep pothole in the track, and the film producer bounced out. You see the roads were not like our roads here. They were not smooth and even with white lines down the middle. They were just made of dirt and stones. They were very uneven and bumpy, and every so often there would be a large hole in the middle of the road. The truck had its sliding doors open, and the film producer was not wearing his seat belt, so when the truck lurched into the hole, he was jolted out.

He fell onto the earth and cut the back of his hand on a sharp stone. 'I'll have to have it looked at,' he said. 'Where's the nearest hospital?'

'There isn't a hospital for miles,' said the guide. 'But there's a small clinic I could take you to. It's not far away.'

The film producer wrapped a clean cloth around his hand and climbed back into the truck and they set off towards the clinic. About an hour later they arrived at a low building made of concrete blocks. 'It doesn't look much like a clinic to me,' said the film producer. They went inside and explained what had happened. 'So I'd like you to clean up my hand please and put a bandage on it. It's a bit painful, so perhaps you could give me a pill for the pain,' said the producer.

The doctor washed the man's hand in some clean water.

'I'm afraid I can't give you a bandage,' he said. 'I used the last one two weeks ago and now I've none left. And we have no painkillers. We've never had any of those here.'

'You mean you've no bandages and not even an aspirin?' said the producer. 'So what do you do when the people who live round here come to you for help?'

'I can't really help them,' said the doctor. 'We have no medicines, no bandages, no equipment for operations. Nothing. We just have to make do with what we can.'

'But that's dreadful,' said the producer. 'And what about my hand? If I don't have proper medical help, it might get an infection in it. I might become ill. What are you going to do?'

'I'm sorry,' said the doctor. 'I can't do anything except try to keep it clean.'

That night the film producer and the guide slept at the clinic. The man's hand was by now very painful. It was swollen and red. He knew that if he had been at home he would have had it properly cleaned and possibly stitched. He knew that he would have been given pills to take away the pain, and an injection to keep infection away. He felt ill and hot and uncomfortable and frightened. He was scared that he might die.

He didn't sleep very well that night. Every time he went to sleep, the pain in his hand woke him up again. He tried to think of all the happiest things he could think of to cheer himself up. He thought of parties and fun, laughter and singing. He thought of comedy programmes on the television, and clowns at the circus.

And then he had his idea!

Clowns! Red noses! Fun!

What if all his friends back home had a fun day when they could pay some money to dress up? If they did that, they would have a good time, but they would also raise some money which they could then send to help the people at this clinic.

By the time the morning came, the idea had grown and grown, and the film producer wondered if it would be possible for hundreds of people to join in, and not just his friends.

Suddenly his hand seemed not to hurt quite so much, and he didn't feel nearly so ill and sorry for himself. He thanked the doctor for trying to help him, and he set off again for the airport and for home.

When he got home he started to make plans for the first Red Nose Day. It was a huge success and another was planned for the next year. And the next. And the next.

Red Nose Day had arrived.

If you watch television today, you'll see lots of people having fun and wearing red noses, and you'll know that they are trying to raise money to help people in Africa. If you look very carefully, you might see one of the television men with a small scar on the back of his hand. If you do, you'll know it was the man in the story who thought up the whole idea in the first place. Keep watching!

Prayer
Dear God, thank you for fun and laughter and happiness. Help us to know that some people in our world don't have as much to be happy about as we do. Help us to help them in whatever ways we can.

Amen

Hymn
'When I needed a neighbour' *Come and Praise* Vol 1

Practical ideas
Comic Relief's basic aim is to fight poverty and to raise funds for work in Africa and the UK. In addition to its fund-raising activities, it aims to raise awareness and promote discussion around the issues it supports.

To this end, Comic Relief has produced a teaching aid – *Teacher Relief*, which is its first structured venture into schools. Teacher Relief consists of a video and workpack, which can be dipped into or followed in depth. It is geared to Key Stages 2 and 3 of the National Curriculum (ages 8 to 13), and covers work across geography, science, technology, English, maths and art. Many of the issues are ideal for raising in personal and social education, and extracts from the video can be used for assemblies.

Teacher Relief is available from Charity Projects, Education Department, 7 Great Russell Street, London WC1B 3NN.

Biblical references to the theme   Week 10   Kindness

'You do yourself a favour when you are kind. If you are cruel, you only hurt yourself.'

Proverbs 11:17

'. . . So then, you must clothe yourselves with compassion, kindness, humility, gentleness, and patience.'

Colossians 3:12

'To conclude: you must all have the same attitude and the same feelings; love one another as brothers, and be kind and humble with one another.'

1 Peter 3:8

April Fool's Day

The first day of April is a 'fun' day; it is celebrated in many countries of the world, especially in Europe. People are tricked or sent on silly errands, but only during the morning. If you try to make an April Fool of someone after midday – *you* become the Fool!

No-one quite knows how April Fool's Day started. Some say it was when Noah sent out the dove the first time, and there was no dry land for it to find. Other people say it is to do with the end of winter and the start of spring. There's an old rhyme about 1st April:

> 'The first of April some do say
> Is set apart for All Fools Day;
> But why the people call it so
> Nor you, nor I, nor anyone know.
> But on this day are people sent
> On errands of pure merriment.
> Although the day is known before,
> There is always a great store
> Of these forgetfuls to be found.'

The secret of having a happy April Fool's Day is to join in the fun, but to make sure your fun isn't unkind to anyone. The teacher in today's story didn't want to join in the fun, even though her children weren't doing anything unkind.

Miss King had rung the school bell and her children were lining up in the school playground. Lots of them had already tried to trick her into being an April Fool, but she was determined she was not going to be tricked.

'Miss King, there's a spider on your shoulder!'

'Miss King, come and see what's in my bag!'

'We're not doing any work today, are we Miss!'

But Miss King kept her eyes straight ahead, and took no notice of any of the comments. She knew what day it was, and she wasn't going to be fooled. She led her class along the corridor towards their classroom. Through the long corridor windows they could see the car park where all the teachers put their cars. Miss King always parked her car the third from the end. The children talked quietly as they walked along, some of them were still trying to catch her out with their April Fool jokes.

'Jeremy's brought his pet mouse to school. He's going to put it in his desk.'

'What will you say to him, Miss?'

•

Lots of the children started to giggle, but Miss King continued up the corridor, her eyes straight ahead, her face unsmiling.

Suddenly, one of the children shouted very loudly, 'Look, Miss King, your car's running away backwards across the car park.'

'That's enough now,' said Miss King. 'We don't shout in school.'

'I know Miss, but your car . . .'

'That's enough I said.'

'But Miss King.'

'Your car, Miss King.'

'It's moving Miss, look.'

'It really is, it's not an April Fool. Look.'

But Miss King was determined not to be caught out by the April Fool joke. She looked straight ahead and took no notice of what the children were saying. By now they had reached the classroom door and they all went inside. The children went to their places, they had work to do. Miss King got out the register and called their names.

She noticed that they were very quiet. No-one was trying to April Fool anyone any more. They kept glancing at her with worried faces. A few minutes later the headteacher came in to the room. He spoke to Miss King and she hurried out. He stayed with the children until she came back.

'Is it about her car?' someone asked.

'What do you know about it?' said Mr Arkwright.

'We saw it,' the children said. 'We saw it going backwards all by itself across the car park.'

'Then why on earth didn't you say something?' said Mr Arkwright.

'We did, but Miss King thought we were April Fooling her, so she didn't take any notice. She wouldn't even look.'

'It was kind of you to try and warn her about the car. I think she must have parked it without putting the handbrake on,' said Mr Arkwright. 'It then rolled gently across the yard and bumped into the low wall at the far side. Luckily no-one was in the way, and there's not much damage, just a scratched bumper and a few broken bricks. No broken bones, that's the main thing.'

Just then Miss King came back. 'I'm sorry I didn't listen to you,' she said. 'I thought you were April Fooling me. But thank you for being kind and trying to tell me about my car.'

Sometimes it's hard to tell the difference between a joke and reality. Perhaps if Miss King had been able to join in the fun of April Fool's Day with the children at the beginning of the story, she might have noticed when they were telling the truth. Then she might have seen the runaway car and been able to stop it before it bumped into the wall. I think the children were having fun in a kind way. They weren't playing cruel or hurtful April Fool tricks, were they? Remember, if you have fun, it must be fun for everyone, and mustn't be fun at someone else's expense.

Prayer

Dear God, thank you for fun days. Help us to be happy and to help other people to be happy too, on fun days. Help us to remember never to have fun at someone else's expense.

Amen

Hymn
'April Fool'   *Harlequin*

The toy kangaroo   *Week 10   Kindness*
adapted from a news item in the Yorkshire Post

It's quite easy to be kind and helpful to someone you know and see every day. It's not so easy to be kind and generous to someone you don't know and have never seen. But the man in today's story managed to be very kind to someone he'd never met, who lived at the other side of the world.

The man was a lorry driver and he lived in Australia. One day he was going to buy a newspaper and he passed the window of a toy shop. The man had no children of his own; he had no nephews and nieces and had no children living next door to him. In fact he didn't really know any children at all, so he had no reason to look in the toy shop window. But something in the window caught his eye.

It was a lovely toy kangaroo. It was standing up on its hind legs, and had a pair of boxing gloves on its front paws.

'I wish I had someone I could buy that for,' said the man. And that's when he had the idea.

'If I can't buy it for a child I know; then I'll buy it for a child I *don't* know!' And the man walked into the shop and bought the toy kangaroo.

He put it in the cab of his lorry, and he wrote a label to hang round its neck. 'This kangaroo is to be given to the nearest child on Christmas Day.' Then he set off for the coast with his lorry load of goods. When he arrived at the port his goods were transferred to a ship, and the toy kangaroo went too. The man drove his lorry back home.

And that was the start of a long long journey, lasting many months, for the toy kangaroo. It was taken across the sea to India, then overland into Pakistan. It travelled through Iran and Turkey, and over the sea to Greece.

It went through Yugoslavia and Switzerland, on to France, and into England. Everywhere it went, lorry drivers asked what it was for. Then they read the label round its neck and knew it was a present. For someone. Somewhere. On Christmas Day. A present because a lorry driver in Australia was kind.

On Christmas Eve, the toy kangaroo was in the cab of a lorry driving north up the M1. The driver had been given the kangaroo in Portsmouth that morning.

'You'll probably be the one to deliver it to where it's going,' the loader had said.

'But where *is* it going?' asked the man.

'To whichever child it's near on Christmas Day.'

'But how will I know?'

'Just take it.'

And so this lorry driver had it in his cab. It was getting late now. The driver wanted to be home for the start of Christmas, but it didn't look as though he was going to make it in time. There were still many miles to go. Perhaps he could just forget about the toy. After all, he didn't have to deliver it. It wasn't his responsibility. Anyway, he didn't know where to take it.

He turned off the M1 into Leeds. Another hour and he should be home. It was ten minutes to twelve now. Nearly Christmas. Nearly home. He drove along the dark streets. In front of him was the clock tower of Seacroft Hospital. He looked at the clock to check the time, and as he looked, the clock struck twelve, and at the same time hundreds of church bells began to ring to herald the start of Christmas.

The driver looked again at the clock and looked at the toy kangaroo. He stopped his lorry and parked it at the edge of the road. He picked up the toy kangaroo and walked through the hospital gate.

'Have you got a child in here?' he asked. Of course he had to explain the whole story of the lorry driver in Australia, and the toy kangaroo's journey across the world, and how it had to be delivered to the nearest child on Christmas Day.

'This is Alan,' said the nurse. 'He's just come into hospital today. He's got a virus, and he's not very well, but we'll soon have him better again.'

'Hello Alan,' said the driver. 'Look what I've got for you. This toy kangaroo has come all the way from Australia to say Happy Christmas and Get Well Soon.'

And that's how Alan, in Leeds, had an extra Christmas present, all because a lorry driver had a kind thought, and a great many other people helped his idea to work.

That's a true story that appeared in the local newspaper. Perhaps we can all try to do something kind for someone, just like the lorry driver in the story.

Prayer
Help us, Lord, to be kind. Help us to be kind to people we know, and kind to those we do not know. Help us to do what we can to spread kindness round the world.

Amen

Hymn
'Think, think on these things'   *Someone's singing Lord*

Practical ideas
This assembly came to life further with the addition of a large world map pinned where everyone could see it. As the story progressed, an older child plotted the toy kangaroo's journey from Australia to England on the map. The story was in fact made longer because we included every lorry and ferry journey and the conversations which took place between drivers at each change-over. The assembly resulted in our older children doing further work on world-wide shipping lanes and road routes.

Not everyone can win   *Week 10   Kindness*

What are you good at? Do you think you could win a competition at it? Some of you will think yes, and some of you will think no to that last question. Perhaps you're like the little girl in this story, who thought she could never win anything.

The fire brigade had been to school and the children had been able to see the engine and talk to the firemen. One of them – a lady – had asked the children to paint some pictures of the engine and the firepeople. She said they would make it into a competition and the winner would win a model fire engine.

Tamsin looked at the beautiful engine and decided she just must win it. She went home at the end of the day and told her dad all about it.

'And I'm quite good at painting, so I might win it, mightn't I? I would like it.'

'Yes, you might win it,' said her Dad. 'But you mustn't be too disappointed if you don't. After all, most of the other children in your class probably want to win it as well, and they're probably good painters too.'

'Yes, but I really want to win,' said Tamsin.

'I know you do,' said her Dad.

Tamsin got out her paints after tea, and started her picture. But somehow she couldn't get it quite right. She knew exactly what she wanted it to look like, but the wheels went wobbly and the helmets were not the right shade of yellow. She began to get cross with it.

'Just do your best,' said her Dad. 'Just do your best.'

Tamsin took her painting to school the next day. The teacher pinned them all to the wall in the morning, and in the afternoon the firepeople came back to judge them. Tamsin sat in her seat with her fingers crossed. She could see the lovely model engine for the winner on the teacher's desk.

'And I think the prize must go to this picture,' said the firelady, pointing to Hussein's painting. Hussein smiled and collected the fire engine. Everyone clapped and said well done. The picture was very good.

Tamsin tried not to be too disappointed, but it was hard. When she got home that afternoon, she burst into tears.

'It's not fair,' she said to her Dad. 'I wanted so much to win. I never win anything. I didn't win this, and I didn't win a medal at dancing class, *and* I didn't win anything at the swimming gala.'

'Come here,' said her Dad. 'Listen to me. Not everyone can win. Not everyone can be a prizewinning painter, or the best dancer, or a famous swimmer. I'd like to be a rich footballer, or the Prime Minister, or even the King. But not everyone can be those things. But . . . everyone can be kind. And you can be kind. All right, you might not be the best painter, but you can be a kind person, and I think that's more important. What do you think?'

And Tamsin smiled and said yes. She was still disappointed about the competition, but she understood what her Dad said.

I wonder what you think. Would you rather be the best painter in the world, but a horrible person; or a really kind person who's nice to know, and who can paint a bit? I know what I think.

Prayer

Dear God, please help us to know that we cannot all be the best at everything; but we can all do our best to be kind to other people.

Amen

Hymn

'Magic Penny'   *Alleluya*

Biblical references to the theme

'Let us try to know the Lord. He will come to us as surely as the day dawns, as surely as the spring rains that water the earth.'

Hosea 6:3

'Ask the Lord for rain in the spring of the year. It is the Lord who sends rain clouds and showers, making the fields green for everyone.'

Zechariah 10:1

The parable of the sower.

Matthew 13:1-23

Peregrine falcons

I wonder what are the first things you think of when I say the word 'spring'? Perhaps you think of daffodils, or lambs, or baby birds, or sunshine, or longer days. All those are signs of the new life of spring. Perhaps you've seen birds collecting materials for their nests. You can see birds almost everywhere, whether you live in a town or a city, and whether you have a garden or not.

Two years ago there was a great deal of commotion on a moor in Yorkshire, because two birds were building a nest. But these were no ordinary birds, these were peregrine falcons.

The farmer's wife was the first to see them. They were looping and circling and diving high in the sky above Ripponden Moor. She didn't know what they were straight away. She knew they were birds of prey, of course, but not until she looked in her bird book did she know that they were peregrine falcons.

The next day she noticed them again. And then she realised they were probably nesting. Peregrines usually nest on cliffs by the sea, so it was quite a surprise to see them here, in the middle of the moor, 50 miles from the sea.

She watched them every day for the next week. She got out her binoculars and saw that they were building a nest on a high ledge in the old quarry. The nest was hardly a nest at all really, just a scraped out hollow in the rocky shelf.

And then she told her husband and her father about the peregrine falcons in the quarry. And the argument began.

'Shoot them,' said her father. 'Destroy the eggs.'

'Don't be silly,' said her husband. 'Peregrines are protected now, like all falcons. It's against the law to kill them.'

'Do you know that peregrines used to kill pigeons during the war?' said her father. 'Homing pigeons used to carry secret messages and peregrines used to kill them. So peregrines deserve to be shot.'

'They deserve nothing of the kind,' said her husband. 'They deserve to be protected, like all wild creatures. And I'm going to see that they are!'

He stormed out of the room, and she heard him using the telephone. He rang the headquarters of the RSPB, and the next day two landrovers and a truck arrived on the moor. In no time, a large hide had been built, right on the edge of the quarry, overlooking the cliff where the peregrines were nesting. The site was so wild and windswept that the wooden building had to be tied down with strong ropes to wooden stakes and boulders, to stop it blowing away into the quarry.

'And what good do you think that's going to do?' her father asked.

'That hide means people can come and see the birds,' said her husband. 'People who have never seen peregrine falcons ever before can come and see them, without disturbing them. People can come and see how beautiful they are, they can understand how they live, then they'll not be like you and want to kill them.'

During the next four weeks, lots of people came every day to sit in the hide and watch the peregrines. The birds were not disturbed because they couldn't see the human beings. The farmer's wife went each day, and eventually she persuaded her father to go along with her.

The hide was quite crowded that day; there were lots of people watching. There was an RSPB warden in the hide as well, with books and information about the peregrines. There were telescopes and binoculars to look through.

Suddenly, a murmur of excitement hummed through the hide. The male peregrine, which had been circling high in the sky, suddenly saw a smaller bird. It snapped back its wings and dropped in a wind-whistling swoop of 180 miles-an-hour. Its talons caught the small bird and killed it outright. The peregrine then flew with its prey to the nest-ledge. And there, huddling with their mother were three fluffy baby peregrine falcons waiting to be fed.

'Do you still think peregrines should be shot?' whispered the farmer's wife.

'No,' said her father. 'They're too beautiful to deserve that.'

That story is true. A great many people had the chance to see the nesting peregrine falcons, because the RSPB put up hides so that they could be seen.

Spring is a time of new life. We need to remember to do what we can to protect all new life.

Prayer

Thank you God, for Spring. Thank you for new life. Help us to protect new life and to do nothing to destroy it.

Amen

Hymn

'All things which live below the sky'   *Someone's singing, Lord*

Practical ideas

Further information on birds is available from the Royal Society for the Protection of Birds, The Lodge, Sandy, Bedfordshire, SG19 2DL, who also run a Young Ornithologists Club. Information and illustrations of peregrine falcons can be found in the *Reader's Digest Field Guide to the Birds of Britain*, published by Hodder and Stoughton (ISBN 0 340 25890 X).

Sowing seeds   *Week 11   Spring*
adapted from the Bible

How many of you have a garden? Spring is the time when we plant seeds. Perhaps your parents have been buying packets of seeds in the supermarkets and garden centres. I know that lots of you have a piece of garden of your own, and maybe you've planted your own seeds. Different seeds need to be planted in different months, depending what type they are. Some seeds can't be planted outside straight away, they have to be grown indoors first. If you were a farmer, you'd plant your seed for the corn in the spring. Today I have a story about corn seed, that Jesus told.

The farmer watched the weather very carefully. It had been raining for several days, and he knew that when the rain stopped, the earth would be soft enough for planting.

The next day the weather was dry and he began to plough the field. He moved up and down, slowly and carefully, ploughing deep, straight furrows in the rich soil. There was a tricky part near the corner of the field that posed a bit of a problem. A footpath cut across the land, and the farmer was careful not to plough it up.

When the furrows were made, he went to collect the seed.

'Can I come and help with the planting?' asked his son.

'Yes,' said the farmer, 'but you'll have to do it carefully.'

They set off side by side with the basket of seed and scattered it as evenly as they could in the centre of each furrow. When they reached the corner of the field where the footpath was, the boy noticed that lots of his seed had fallen on the path.

'Shall I pick it up and then it won't be wasted?' he asked.

'No,' said the farmer. 'There's no need. The corn won't grow there, but the birds will eat the seed. Just leave it.' So the boy did.

It took a long time to scatter all the seed, but at last it was done, and the farmer went along each of the furrows again to cover the seed with a layer of soil. Then there was nothing to do but to wait.

Several days later the boy noticed the first green shoots poking through the earth. 'It's growing,' he told his dad.

'I should hope it is,' said the farmer.

The boy checked on the new growing corn every day. Some of it seemed to be growing very well, but one small patch was becoming thin and weak.

'What's the matter with it?' he asked.

'There's a rock there, just under the soil,' said his father. 'That corn won't grow because it can't get its roots down into the soil.'

'And why has that corn got so many leaves?' said the boy, pointing to a bushy growth near the edge of the field.

'Those leaves don't belong to the corn plants,' said the farmer. 'Look; this plant is a bush. Some of the corn seed must have fallen on the soil where the bush is growing, and now the corn plants are all mixed up with the bush.'

'Will they grow up together?' asked the boy.

'No, I'm afraid not,' said the farmer. 'The bush is stronger than the new corn plants, and it'll take all the food from the earth and choke them. The young corn plants in there will die.'

'Will *any* of the corn grow?' said the boy.

'Of course it will,' laughed his dad. 'All the corn that's growing in the good soil will grow into strong plants.'

And sure enough, with sun and rain and time, the corn that had been planted in good soil, grew tall and healthy.

Jesus told that story to teach people about themselves. He said that people are like the corn seed. He said that people who don't listen to God, are like the seeds that fell on the path. He said that people who listen, but don't let the message sink in, are like the seeds that fell on the rocky ground.

He said that people who listen to God, but then let other things get in the way of them taking any notice, are like the seeds that fell in the bushes.

But he said that people who listen to God and try to do as he asks, are like the seeds that fell on the good soil and grew tall and strong.

Prayer
Thank you God, for spring time. Thank you for seeds and soil, for sun and rain. Thank you for gardens and farms. Help us to look after all growing things. Help us to grow strong, so that we can do what is right.

Amen

Hymn
'It happens each Spring'   *Harlequin*

Mothering Sunday
Week 11   Spring
The date of Mothering Sunday varies each year because Easter is a movable feast. Mothering Sunday is always the fourth Sunday in Lent.

Mothering Sunday always comes during the serious time before Easter. In olden days, when girls used to leave home to go and work as servants in big houses, Mothering Sunday was a cheerful day when they were allowed to go home to visit their mothers. They used to take a present of a simnel cake, or a bunch of wild flowers. Nowadays, we celebrate Mothering Sunday by giving our mums cards and presents, and by trying to give her a rest, as well.

The boy in today's story tried to help his mum on Mothering Sunday, but I'll be interested to hear what you think about him!

Mrs Hunak was spring cleaning. She knew that lots of people don't bother with a good old-fashioned spring clean nowadays, but she liked to do it; or rather she liked it when it was finished.

Dan was in his bedroom when the trouble started. He was actually making his mum a card for Mothers' Day, and then he was going to get her present ready, but he didn't want her to know anything about the present or the card until Sunday.

'Dan, can you come out of your room now. I want to take your curtains down and wash the windows. And I want to change your bed. I can't get on with you in there. Come on out now.'

'Oh Mum!' said Dan. 'I can't stop what I'm doing just now. Can't you do my room later. I'm busy.'

'No I can not,' his mum called. 'I've lots to do. I want all this cleaning finished by the weekend. Come on now. You're holding me up.'

'Aw Mum!'

'Come ALONG! You're wasting my time. You could help me you know, instead of messing about in there.'

'I'm not messing about,' shouted Dan, feeling very annoyed because he knew he was doing something nice for his Mum. He gathered all his things together and stuffed them into an empty box, then came out of his room.

'What are you going to do now?' asked his mum. 'You could tidy your room, that would help me. Will you do that?'

'Sorry Mum,' said Dan. 'I can't just now. I'm busy.' and he disappeared down the garden to his dad's greenhouse. He'd been growing some plants for Mothers' Day, and he was going to put the best ones into a china plantholder and give it to his mum on Sunday. His dad had shown him what to do, and had left the potting compost and everything ready. Dan had bought a lovely china pot and it was waiting, still wrapped in the shop's paper bag, under the greenhouse worktop.

He unwrapped the china pot, filled it with compost, and carefully planted the best of the plants. The lady in the shop had given him a ribbon on a stick, and he pushed it into the soil between the plants. Then he gave the plants a drink of water, the present looked lovely. He knew his mum would be pleased with it. He put it back under the worktop, and went up to the house to finish his card. Perhaps his mum had finished in his bedroom now. He hoped she hadn't looked in the box and seen the card.

'Oh, there you are,' she said when he went through the door. 'You're just in time. Will you get the table ready for tea. Your dad'll be home soon. Tea's on, but I can just finish the stairs if you'll do the table for me.'

'Oh Mum! I'm busy. I've got things to do.'

'You are a selfish boy,' his mum shouted. 'Here am I, doing all this work to make the house clean and tidy, and you can't do anything to help. Just you wait 'till your dad gets home . . .'

'But Mum, it's not like that. It's not fair.'

'I know it's not fair,' said his mum. 'Nothing's been fair to me all day.'

And then, right in the middle of them shouting at each other, Dan's dad came home.

'What on earth is going on?' he said. And they both told him.

The story doesn't say what happened next. Perhaps Dan's dad told him off. Or perhaps he thought the argument was Dan's mum's fault. I wonder what *you* think?

I think it was a pity that Dan couldn't have helped his mum, even though he was busy doing something nice for her. I hope you are helpful and kind to your mums all the year round, and not just on Mothering Sunday.

Prayer

Thank you God, for our mothers and the people who care for us. Help us to remember to say thank you to them, for all the things they do for us.

Remind us to be helpful to them during the year, and not just on Mothering Sunday.

Amen

Hymn
'Now thank we all our God' *Come and Praise* Vol 1

Biblical references to the theme   Week 12   Easter

The Easter story can be found in all four gospels: Matthew chapter 27 and 28; Mark chapter 15 and 16; Luke chapter 23 and 24; John chapter 19 and 20.

The legend of the bells   Week 12   Easter

Did you know that Easter is the oldest Christian festival? And did you know that Easter Sunday doesn't always fall on the same date? The early churches couldn't agree on the date it should be celebrated, and then, 1700 years ago, the Council of Nicaea decided how it should be chosen, and it's been that way ever since.

Easter Sunday is always the Sunday after the first full moon which comes after the vernal equinox. (That's the Spring day when day and night are of equal length; usually on March 21st.) It's a complicated way of working out a date, and it depends on the sun and moon. It means that Easter Day can fall at any time between March 21st and April 25th. It's not a fixed date like Christmas, which always falls on December 25th.

Easter is celebrated all over the world, and there are many stories and legends about it. Today I have a legend for you from Italy.

Maria and Ricardo lived in a small village in the mountains of northern Italy. It was the week before Easter and everything was very quiet. There were no festivities this week, no sweet food, no fun. Even the church looked sad. Inside, the usually gleaming golden cross and all the paintings of the Saints were covered with dark purple cloths.

'Why does everything look so dark and miserable?' Maria asked her mother.

'Because it's Holy Week and it's a serious and solemn time,' she said.

'Even the bells have stopped ringing,' said Ricardo. 'They always ring every morning and evening to tell people it's time for church. Why have they stopped?'

Their mother looked at the children. 'Don't you know?' she asked. 'The bells have flown away to Rome to see the Pope!'

The children laughed. 'Bells don't fly,' they said.

'Easter bells do,' she said. 'They fly away to Rome the week before Easter. You listen across the valley; you'll not hear a church bell ring this week.'

During the next few days, the children listened carefully every time they went outside. But, sure enough, not one single bell did they hear.

'When will they fly back?' they asked their mother.

'On Easter Day,' she said. 'And they'll not come alone. They'll bring something with them!'

'What?' asked the children; but their mother would not say.

They waited impatiently through the rest of the week. Maundy Thursday. Good Friday. Holy Saturday. Each day the people of the village went to church, but they went when their clocks said, not when the bells rang. The bells remained silent.

At last it was Easter Sunday. The sun shone and the women of the village were up early. They hurried to the church. They took the purple covers from the golden cross and the pictures, and they arranged huge bunches of flowers in all the vases. They put a white cloth covered in gold embroidery on the altar. Then they went home again to put on their best clothes.

Suddenly the air was filled with the sound of bells, ringing across the valleys and echoing from the mountains.

'They're back,' shouted Ricardo. 'The bells have come back from Rome.'

'Where have they been and what have they brought?' said Maria.

'They're home again in their bell tower,' said their mother. 'And to know what they've brought, you must hurry to the church door. Go along. Hurry.'

Maria and Ricardo ran out of the house and down the street. They met all the other children of the village, who, at the first sound of the bells, were also hurrying to the church door.

And there on the steps were the baskets. Dozens of them. One for every boy and girl. Decorated with ribbons and flowers and filled with straw.

'Baskets of straw?' said Maria. 'The bells have brought us baskets of straw?'

Ricardo picked up his basket from the step.

'No,' he said. 'Look.' And there, nestling in the straw of each basket, were eggs. Beautiful sugar fondant eggs, each the size of a hen's egg, but blue or white or pink or yellow.

'Thank you bells,' the children shouted. 'Thank you for our eggs.'

And the bells pealed out 'Hap-py Eas-ter Day to you and Hap-py Eas-ter Day to you and Hap-py Eas-ter Day to you-ou,' over and over again.

Children all over the world have eggs on Easter Day. Sometimes the eggs are brought by the Easter rabbit, or the Easter hare, or the Easter bells, but they all bring the same happy message of Easter. I wonder who will bring *you* an egg this Easter?

Prayer
Thank you God, for Easter. Thank you for Easter stories and Easter eggs. Thank you for the happiness and joy of Easter. Help us each to do our share of spreading happiness this Easter.

Amen

Hymn
'Jesus Christ is here'   *Come and Praise* Vol 1

Eggs around the world   *Week 12   Easter*

Do you think you will be having an egg for Easter? I think most of you will be given a chocolate egg or two on Sunday.

Do you know why we have eggs for Easter? Because Easter is a time of new life, and eggs are a sign of new life. The children in today's story found out that the egg is a sign of new life nearly everywhere in the world, and not just in Britain.

They met every year for a holiday: The Children's International Summer Village. They were chosen from different schools all over the world; boys and girls to represent their own country, to go on holiday together.

At first they were shy of each other, and talking was difficult because they didn't speak each others' languages. But soon everyone got to know everyone else as they all made friends.

They learned about each others' way of life, and food, and customs, and clothes, and homes. And one year, they found out about each others' eggs!

It happened quite by chance when Peter from England mentioned chocolate Easter eggs.

'What are those?' asked Alinka from Poland.

'We eat them on Easter Sunday,' said Peter. 'They're big eggs made of chocolate. Don't you have them?'

'No,' said Alinka. 'We have Easter eggs, but they're not made of chocolate, they're real eggs called "psyanki". It means "written eggs". They're beautiful. You draw a pattern on them in hot wax, then you dip them in coloured ink. Then you melt off the wax and you're left with a lovely lacy patterned egg.'

'We have eggs like that, too,' said Kurt from Holland. 'But they're made differently. We dye the eggs in lovely colours, then scratch a pattern on with a needle. The white eggshell shows through in a lacy pattern.'

'We don't have Easter eggs,' said Chen from China. 'But we give eggs as presents to the parents of a new baby.'

'We give coloured eggs to each other on the first day of Spring,' said Solmaz. She came from Iran.

'We have coloured eggs too,' said Heidi from Germany. 'Our mothers dye hens' eggs in different colours, then they hide them in the garden. On Easter Sunday my brothers and sisters play hide and seek for the eggs. The one who finds the most eggs gets a prize. But my mum always gives each one of us a prize.'

'We give each other Easter gifts,' said Vanya. She was from Russia. 'A hundred years ago, rich people in Russia used to give each other beautiful jewelled eggs made of silver and gold and decorated with sparkling jewels. The eggs used to open and there would be a tiny gift inside. But we don't give each other gifts like that now; it would cost too much money.'

'Our eggs don't cost very much at all,' said Brett. He lived in America. 'We have an egg roll on Easter Day.'

'What's that?' asked the others.

'It's a competition,' said Brett. 'Our moms make some hard-boiled eggs for us, then on Easter morning we all go to the hill near my house and roll our eggs down it.'

'What happens then?' said Solmaz.

'We see whose egg goes furthest without breaking,' said Brett. 'Then that person's egg is the winner and they win a prize.'

'It sounds great fun,' said Chen. 'Let's have an egg roll now!'

So all the children went to the kitchen and asked the cook for lots of hard-boiled eggs. He was very surprised, but ten minutes later he gave them 24 eggs to share between the eight of them.

They went outside to the small hill at the edge of the playing field, and spent the whole afternoon rolling eggs and having a lot of fun.

I wonder which child won the egg rolling competition? Perhaps the children weren't bothered about who won – perhaps they just had fun playing together and taking turns. I'm glad they all got along so well together, even though they were all from different parts of the world, with different customs and traditions.

Prayer

Dear God, thank you for all the different countries of the world. Thank you for their different languages, customs and traditions. Help us to know that the world is one big family. Help us to understand our world neighbours. Help us to learn from them and they from us, especially this Easter time.

Amen

Hymn

'Silver trumpet'   *Alleluya*

The legend of the Easter rabbit   *Week 12   Easter*

In yesterday's assembly, Peter, the boy from England, said that children in Britain are often given chocolate eggs at Easter, but he didn't tell the other children about the Easter rabbit. Do you know about the Easter rabbit?

Many children in European countries are told that Easter eggs are brought by the Easter rabbit. Here's the legend of how it started.

Once upon a time when the Christ Child was alive, the earth began to die. Oh, the sun still shone and the seasons came and went, but nothing seemed to try hard any more. The birds forgot to sing and the flowers forgot to bloom; the trees stood stiffly still and the people said, 'There's no point in working hard any more.'

The Christ Child said, 'You must not give up hope. The earth will not die. I am here to bring new life. I need a messenger to go and tell this to the world. Who will help me?'

The animals clamoured to be the chosen messenger.

'Choose me! Choose me,' they said.

The Christ Child knew it would be impossibly unfair to choose any one animal in preference to any other, so he said 'Whichever one of you can travel fastest round the world can be my messenger.'

'It will be me,' declared the deer.

'I'll do it fastest,' said the salmon.

'The job's as good as mine,' sang the eagle.

'Perhaps I'll be the first,' whispered the rabbit. And the creatures set off: leaping, swimming, swooping, running, each in his own preferred way.

The deer was off to a good start. She leapt, sure-footed across the land. But then she met some others, jumping over crags and streams and having a fine time. She stopped to play . . . and soon time disappeared.

The salmon started well. He swam strongly downstream, towards the open sea. But once there, he saw sunbeams dancing on the waves like golden pennies. He stopped to play . . . and soon time disappeared.

The eagle, too, began with speed. She soared high over the mountain tops towards more distant lands. But, when high in the sky, she noticed a tiny foreign field mouse, down, scuttling round. She swooped and dived and stopped to play . . . and soon time disappeared.

The rabbit hopped. Then paused for breath, looking round, ears turning, nose twitching. Then hopped some more. Quickly on. White scut flashing. Hop and hop. Stop. Hop and hop. On and on. Steadily. Carefully. Round the world and back.

'Well done. Bravo! The first one home,' cried the Christ Child when he saw the rabbit. 'You shall be my messenger.'

But the rabbit felt suddenly shy.

'How will anyone believe me?' he said. 'No-one will take any notice of me. They'll not believe what I say.'

'Take this,' said the Christ Child, and he handed the rabbit a brown egg, still warm from the hen. 'Take this as a sign of new life, and tell the world that as surely as the egg is new life, so am I.'

The rabbit took the small warm brown egg and looked at it. Its new-life promise was safe inside; everyone knew that. The rabbit waved goodbye to the Christ Child and set off again around the world. This time with the Christ Child's message of new life and hope.

Everywhere he went he left an egg. One for each mother and father, daughter and son. Everywhere. In every village and town.

After many years of travelling, the rabbit returned to the place where he had last seen the Christ Child. He asked where he was. 'He'll be a grown man now,' he said.

'The man died on a cross,' they said. 'His body is in a dark cave. You're too late. You can't help him now.'

'No,' said the rabbit. 'You're wrong. *He's* here to help *us*. He promised hope and new life. Look!' And he showed them an egg.

And the people understood. The next day they heard the news that the Christ Man was indeed alive.

'You're a good messenger,' he said to the rabbit. But already the rabbit was gone. Gone again around the world with his message of hope and new life, hidden in an egg.

Perhaps the Easter rabbit will visit your house with an egg. But perhaps it will be a chocolate egg instead of a small warm brown hen's egg.

Prayer

Thank you God, for Easter. Thank you for its promise of hope and new life.

Amen

Hymn

'All in an Easter Garden'   *Come and Praise* Vol 2

Summer Term

Biblical references to the theme *Week 1 Thinking ahead*

'Sensible people always think before they act, but stupid people advertise their ignorance.'

Proverbs 13:16

'I, the Lord, the God of Israel, warn you not to let yourselves be deceived . . . or by any others who claim they can predict the future. Do not pay any attention to their dreams.'

Jeremiah 29:8

Two girls and a box of matches *Week 1 Thinking ahead*

None of us can see into the future. We don't know what is going to happen. But we can think ahead, to make sure that what we do doesn't hurt anyone else. Sometimes it's very easy to get so involved in what we want to do, that we forget that everything everyone does, affects someone else.

There's a school I know, near a big city. The school is for children between the ages of five and 11. There are about 250 children at the school, and about 12 teachers. The school is a very happy one. It's like a big family; everyone knows everyone else, and everyone tries to help everyone else.

Last year, on the very last day of the Easter holiday, two teenage girls were messing about round the back of the school building. They shouldn't have been there. They were both supposed to be at home because they'd been in trouble the day before. They were giggling and being silly with some magazines they were looking at. One girl had some matches.

They weren't *planning* to do any damage. They didn't *decide* to do anything wrong. But somehow, because they didn't think, because they didn't use their brains, because they didn't look ahead, it happened.

The magazines had fallen on the floor by the school wall. One of the girls lit a match, but it burned her fingers, so she dropped it, and then they ran away.

That was it. That's all they did.

You might think that there was nothing wrong in that. But as I said; they didn't think ahead.

They didn't think that the match they dropped on the floor would fall on to the magazines. But it did.

They didn't think that the magazines would smoulder and catch fire. But they did.

And they certainly didn't think that the burning magazines would set the school wall on fire. But they did.

The wall was made of a wooden frame, with tiles hung on it. And the window frame nearby was made of wood. The fire burned through the wooden frames, and the charred hot tiles fell on to the floor. The fire burned through the inside wall of the classroom and got into the school. It burned through the ceiling and destroyed the floor. It consumed the curtains and the wall displays, the bookshelves and the children's tables and chairs. It swept through the classroom and into the corridor, leaving a black, smoking, burning, charred, destroyed classroom behind it.

By now the flames had burned through the roof and were leaping up into the sky. One of the neighbours whose house backed onto the school field saw the fire and telephoned for the fire brigade. It was quickly there, and soon the blaze was under control.

The police rang the headteacher of the school; she was enjoying the last day of the holiday.

'Come to school straight away,' they said. 'There's been a fire.'

She came and saw all the damage. She saw the classroom that was completely destroyed. She saw the door that the firemen had had to break down to get in. She saw the damage from all the water the firemen had had to use. And she saw the damage everywhere in school, in every classroom, from the smoke of the fire. And tomorrow was the first day of the new term. Tomorrow all the children would be back from their holidays.

The headteacher and the teachers, the cleaners and the caretaker, the firemen, the workmen and lots of the children's mums and dads, worked all that day and far into the night to get the school ready for the children the next day. They couldn't get the damaged classroom ready of course, that would take weeks and weeks of work to put right. In the meantime, the children in that class would have to make the school hall into their classroom. But that meant that no other class could have PE, and school dinners had to be moved, and all the assemblies had to be rearranged. All because two silly girls didn't think ahead. They didn't think that their actions would affect anyone else.

At first, the two girls knew nothing about the fire. They ran away as soon as they had dropped the match. They went to a friend's house, quite a long way away from the school. But they knew about it before the end of the day, because the police went round to their houses. And later they had to appear in court to explain what had happened. Later still, they had to go and live at a school for young offenders.

And all that upset and damage and sadness and work happened because two girls didn't think ahead. The only good thing about the whole incident was that no-one was hurt.

Prayer
Help us God, to know that what we do affects other people. Help us to think ahead, and not to do silly, dangerous things that might hurt us or others.

Amen

Hymn
'Think of a world without any flowers'   *Come and Praise* Vol 1

The fox and the cockerel
adapted from Aesop

Week 1   Thinking ahead

In our last assembly, we heard about two girls who caused a lot of damage because they didn't think ahead. In today's story neither the cockerel nor the fox bothered to think ahead. They both had a surprise, but in different ways.

The fox was prowling round a farmyard one day when he saw the cockerel, standing on a fence.

'He'll be just right for my dinner,' thought the fox 'but I'll have to be very clever to trick him into coming near me.'

The fox strolled a little nearer the cockerel.

'Hello,' he said. 'Do you mind if I pay you a compliment? I just want to say that I have never before seen such a fine looking cockerel as you. Well, not since your father of course. He and I were very good friends. He was a really handsome bird, and he had such a fine voice, didn't he!'

'Yes, he did,' said the cockerel. 'But people say I have a fine voice too, a voice to match my father's.'

'Really?' said the fox. 'Well, what a coincidence! I should very much like to hear your fine voice. It would make me feel so happy. Will you crow for me?'

'Certainly. I shall be glad to,' answered the cockerel, and he began to puff himself up, and stand as tall and straight as he could. When he was ready he closed his eyes tightly and began to crow at the top of his voice.

As soon as he did this, the fox leapt forward. He grabbed the cockerel by his neck and rushed off into the fields with him before anyone had time to stop him.

Some men who were working nearby saw what had happened. They threw down their spades and hoes and ran after the fox.

'Stop!' they shouted to him. 'Let go of that cockerel. Put him down.

Stop!' But of course the fox took absolutely no notice and carried on running as fast as all his four legs would carry him.

The cockerel, dangling between the fox's teeth, realised that no-one else would be able to save him, and that if he didn't want to become the fox's next dinner, he would have to save himself.

He twizzled himself round so that he could speak to the fox.

'If I were you,' he said, 'I would tell those men to mind their own business. It's nothing to do with them what you do. Tell them that I belong to you, and then they'll stop chasing you. Go on; tell them.'

'You're right,' said the fox. 'I'll tell . . .' but he never got any further than that, because as soon as he opened his mouth to speak, the cockerel took his chance and flapped away as fast as his wings would wave.

The cockerel flew back to his fence, and the fox walked back to the field.

'In future I'll think before I take notice of anyone who pays me a compliment,' said the cockerel.

'And I'll think before I do something someone else tells me to,' said the fox.

Sometimes we do things because a friend tells us to. It's a good idea to think for yourself before you do anything that anyone tells you to. If you think it's a good idea, then go ahead and do it. If you think it's not a good idea, then say . . . no.

Prayer
Dear God, please help us to think for ourselves. Help us to think ahead and work out for ourselves whether something's a good idea or not.

Amen

Hymn
'Think, think on these things'   *Someone's singing, Lord*

The man who day-dreamed   *Week 1   Thinking ahead*
adapted from the Panchatantra

It's good to plan ahead, and to think ahead, and know what you want to do next; but it's not such a good idea to let your dreams run away with you! If you do, things may not work out quite as you planned. Listen to what happened to the man in today's story. It happened a long time ago.

During the day, he ate his meals at the house of a certain merchant. If by any chance the merchant was out, and couldn't give the man his dinner, he gave him a bag of flour instead. I suppose the idea was that he could make something to eat for himself.

But he didn't. Every time he was given a bag of flour, he emptied it into a jar; and hung the jar – by its string – on a nail in the wall.

One day the man was lying on his bed, having a rest; the flour jar was hanging on its nail, in the wall, above his bed, where it always was. The man started thinking.

'I have a lot of flour in my jar now, and flour is very expensive. I think I'll sell my flour. If I sell it, I should get enough money to buy myself a goat.

'If I buy a she-goat, she'll have a baby in about six months time; and when the baby grows up, she can have a baby of her own. In five years' time, I'll have lots of goats.

'And if I have lots of goats I'll be able to sell them and buy some cows. Cows would make me rich indeed. The cows will have calves, and when they grow up they'll have calves and after another five years I'll have a whole herd of cows.

'If I have a herd of cows I'll be rich enough to have a big farm, and I'll be able to grow corn. I'll sell sacks and sacks of the corn and I'll be able to have a beautiful big mansion house built.

'My house will be so fine and big that lots of servants will want to come and work in it.

'And when all the young ladies see my fine mansion house, and my fine farm, they'll all want to marry me. I'll have a wonderful wedding and my wife will have a lovely baby boy. I'll call him Somasarman.

'He will play outside whilst I work on my farm. I'll show him the farm and teach him how to look after the animals and the fields. He'll learn well and no-one will ever be angry with him.

'But what if one day someone *was* angry with him? That would make me feel angry too. I would chase them away with a stick. I would wave it high in the air and shout at them.'

As the man was thinking these thoughts, he sat up on his bed, grabbed a wooden stick that was propped up against the wall, and brandished it in the air.

The stick crashed against the flour jar, and it smashed into smithereens all over the man, the bed and the floor. The flour fell with a flump on the man, and a great white cloud of it rose up and covered everything.

The neighbours came running in to see what had happened.

'Day-dreaming again?' they laughed. 'You'll never learn will you? This time you've lost your flour because of your day-dreaming. Never mind. We'll help you to clean it up.'

And they did.

There's a saying you might have heard, which goes, 'Don't count your chickens until they're hatched.' It means make sure a thing is really yours, before you make any definite plans for it.

Prayer
Dear God, help us not to be greedy. Help us to know that it's good to plan ahead, but help us not to be too sure . . . until we're certain.

Amen

Hymn
'It's a new day'   *Come and Praise* Vol 2

Biblical references to the theme   *Week 2   People*

'Worship the Lord, all the earth!
Honour him, all peoples of the world!'

Psalms 33:8

'For Christ himself has brought us peace by making Jews and Gentiles one people.'

Ephesians 2:14

'Our people must learn to spend their time doing good, in order to provide for real needs; they should not live useless lives.'

Titus 3:14

Singh – as brave as a lion   *Week 2   People*
adapted from Sikh teaching

There are millions of people on this earth; in some ways we are all different, and in other ways we are all the same. We are all human beings and we all belong to the family of humankind. But if we are all so alike, how do we know who is who? How do we manage not to mix up all our friends? Because, in small ways, we are all different, and of course we all have different names. When we are babies we are given a name that becomes our own.

When Sikh children are baptised, they too are given a special name. But Sikh children are given a second name; a boy is given the name Singh, which means lion, and a girl is given the name Kaur, which means princess. Here is the story of how this came about.

Baisakhi was a special festival to celebrate the Indian harvest, and the start of Guru Nanak's travels. Nearly three hundred years ago, Guru Gobind Singh chose this day to be the birthday of the Sikhs.

Guru Gobind Singh sent messengers throughout India, to tell the Sikh people to gather together on Baisakhi Day. They travelled from far and near, more than a hundred thousand people, and met for morning prayers at Anandpur. They were pleased to have the chance to hear the words of Guru Gobind Singh; he was a kind man who looked after people and tried to help the poor.

Guru Gobind Singh said morning prayers. Then he began to talk about the job of guarding the Holy Book in the Temple. He needed five men to guard it; five men who would be brave and fearless; five men who would be prepared to die if needs be.

Suddenly, Guru Gobind Singh pulled out his sword. Its blade flashed in the bright sunlight.

'Who is brave enough to guard the Holy Book?' he said. 'Who is brave enough to die?'

For several minutes there was not a sound in the huge crowd. No-one spoke. You could have heard a feather fall, it was so quiet. Then one man stepped forward.

'I will,' he said. 'I will guard the Holy Book, even if it means dying, for it would be an honourable death.'

'Come into the Temple,' said Guru Gobind Singh.

The man and the Guru left the crowd.

The crowd waited. They heard the swish of a sword blade. They saw Guru Gobind Singh return to them, but he was alone. The man from the crowd was not with him. In Guru Gobind Singh's hand was his sword, but now it was dripping with blood.

'I need another man,' he said. 'Another, who is prepared to die, as the last one was.'

The crowd stood still. Then there was pandemonium. The people could not believe their eyes or ears. Guru Gobind Singh had always been so kind and gentle, but now he was taking men and killing them.

Even so, another man stepped forward.

'I will die for my faith,' he said.

Guru Gobind Singh took the second man into the Temple, and returned alone a few seconds later. Once more his sword dripped with fresh blood.

He asked the crowd for a third man, and then a fourth, and then a fifth. Each time he asked, there was at first silence, then someone volunteered to go with the Guru, because they trusted him. But each time he took a man into the temple, he came back alone, and each time he came back, the crowd could see, all too clearly, the flashing sword.

After the fifth man had been taken to the Temple, Guru Gobind Singh stood before the crowd and smiled. The people were afraid. But then, the Guru beckoned towards the Temple, and all five men came walking out, quite unharmed.

'These men, who followed me into the Temple,' said the Guru, 'Were as brave as lions. They were prepared to follow me, even though they thought they were going to a certain death. But you can see, they have not been hurt.'

Guru Gobind Singh then baptised the five brave men. After the ceremony, he asked that all Sikh men take the name Singh, meaning lion, as their second name, and that all Sikh women take the name Kaur, meaning princess, as their second name. The Guru said that if everyone took the same name, it would show that everyone is equal and that the human race is one united family.

Sikh men and women try to follow bravely in the steps of Guru Gobind Singh, and the other nine great Gurus before him. They carry their second names of Singh and Kaur with pride, and try to remember that they belong to one great family, the family of mankind.

Baisakhi is celebrated every year, and it usually falls on April 13th.

Prayer
Dear God, please help us to be as brave as lions as we do our work each day. Help us to remember to do our best in everything we do, and to remember that we all belong to the family of mankind, whatever our beliefs and religion.

Amen

Hymn
'The family of man' *Come and Praise* Vol 1

The man who walked to Warsaw
adapted from Jewish fable

Week 2 People

Have you ever noticed that some people always think that other people's things are better than theirs? Some people are always envious of other people; they think that others have better lives, or easier jobs, or more expensive possessions, or bigger houses. Some people always think that life somewhere else would be better than theirs.

In fact, most people eventually discover that their own life is very good, and that the other one they thought was so marvellous, is not so good after all. In today's story, a man wanted very much to know what life in another city was like. He was sure it would be better than his. But he was in for a shock!

The man's name was Geitzel and he lived in the famous city of Chelm, in Poland. Now Chelm, as you might know, is full of very wise people, and Geitzel was no exception.

One day, Geitzel heard some travellers talking about the beautiful city of Warsaw, not far from Chelm. Geitzel had never been to Warsaw, but he thought that life there must be very good, and the city must be very lovely, in fact it was probably better than Chelm; so Geitzel decided to go and see Warsaw for himself.

He said goodbye to Froedel, his wife, and to his six children, and promised to bring them all presents back from the wonderful city of Warsaw. Then he set off.

It was a long walk to Warsaw, and by midday Geitzel was feeling tired. He sat down to rest by the roadside and leaned against a tree. He felt himself begin to drift off to sleep. It wouldn't matter if he had a little rest. He was in no hurry.

But suddenly he sat up again. It didn't matter if he went to sleep for a few minutes, but it did matter if he forgot which way he was going! What if he woke up and accidentally walked back the way he had come? He would never get to Warsaw! He would only walk back to Chelm!

Geitzel jumped to his feet and scratched his head. What to do? What to do?

'That's it!' he thought. 'Boots!' He took off his boots and put them down carefully next to the tree trunk: the toes pointing towards Warsaw and the heels towards Chelm.

'Now I can go to sleep and when I wake up, I'll know which way to go. My boots will tell me.' Geitzel then lay down by the tree and fell fast asleep.

While he was asleep, a cart laden with branches came past. The branches hung down over the side of the cart and swept along the ground. They swept past Geitzel's boots and turned them clean around, to face the other way: the toes towards Chelm, and the heels towards Warsaw. The cart swept on down the lane. Geitzel slept on under the tree.

After about an hour, he woke, stretched, yawned, looked at his boots, and said 'What a good thing I set them down pointing in the right direction, for I've completely forgotten which way I've come.' Geitzel pulled on his boots and set off in the direction the toes were pointing. Towards Chelm!

'Not much further now,' he thought. 'Only a few more miles and I'll be in Warsaw. I can't wait to see it.'

Geitzel walked a little more quickly, and by early evening he came to the edge of the town. And what a surprise he had. Warsaw looked exactly like Chelm! The streets looked the same. The houses looked the same. Even the people looked the same.

'Well!' thought Geitzel. 'Warsaw is a town worth seeing. I feel at home in it already.'

He walked through the streets to the market place. He looked at all the stalls. 'Just like the ones in Chelm,' he thought.

He went to the synagogue. 'Exactly like the one back home,' he said.

Then he walked along the road to where his own house would have been, if he'd been in Chelm, of course. And there it was. An exact double of his house. In exactly the right place.

'Well I never!' he said.

As he stood there, gazing at the extraordinary sight of a house the perfect double of his own, but in the wrong city of course, six children and their mother came tumbling out of the door.

Geitzel stared. They were identical to his own family. This was unbelievable. A house and a family, here in Warsaw, absolutely the same as his own house and family back in Chelm. He rubbed his eyes and pinched his cheek to make sure he wasn't dreaming. But no. Geitzel was truly awake.

Just then, the mother of the children looked up and saw Geitzel standing outside the house.

'Ah, good,' she called. 'Look children. You can have your supper now, Geitzel has come home.'

Geitzel could hardly believe his ears. There was not only a wife that looked like Froedel, and children that looked like his six, there was also a man called Geitzel who looked exactly like himself. A double. A doppelgänger.

Geitzel looked round to see the man who was Geitzel. He so wanted to see his double, here in this strange city of Warsaw. But Geitzel saw no-one.

The lady who looked like Froedel called again.

'Come on in. Supper's ready.'

'Who, me?' said Geitzel.

'Yes, you!' said the Froedel-lady.

Geitzel didn't know what to do. But he was hungry, and he wanted to see the other Geitzel when he came home, so he went into the house. It was exactly like his, inside as well as out. Geitzel discovered that the Froedel-lady cooked meat broth in just the same way as his own Froedel cooked it. Geitzel also discovered that the other Geitzel didn't come home.

He decided to stay in the Warsaw house until the other Geitzel should appear; he so wanted to see him. But the Warsaw Geitzel didn't come that day or the next. He didn't come the next week, or the next month, or the next year.

By now Geitzel was very unhappy. He missed his own dear Froedel and his own children so much. This Froedel and these children in Warsaw were very nice, but they were not *his*. He had now been away from home for so long that he dared not go back. Anyway, he had not bought the presents he'd promised them. If only he hadn't gone away to see the city of Warsaw. He'd have been so much happier if he'd stayed at home!

I don't think Geitzel ever learned the truth. Even if someone had told him what had really happened, I don't think he would have believed them. What a pity he spent the rest of his life feeling miserable.

Prayer

Dear God, thank you for our homes and families. Help us to know that although life in other places may seem exciting, home is usually a good place to come back to.

Amen

Hymn

'At half past three we go home to tea'   *Someone's singing, Lord*

The man and his goat   Week 2   People
adapted from the Panchatantra

It's very difficult being a child, isn't it? I thought you might agree! On the one hand everyone is always telling you what to do; and on the other you are expected to think for yourself, and not just do what someone else tells you! It's quite a problem. The best advice I can give you, is always to think for yourself, and do what *you* think is right. That's hard if everyone seems to think differently from you, but it might be worth sticking to what *you* believe. Listen to what happened in today's story.

A man had a goat and was taking it back to his own village. Perhaps he had bought it in the market, or perhaps he had been trying to sell it; we don't know why he had it – only that he did.

As he was walking along the road, he was watched by three rogues. 'Let's take it from him,' said one of them.

'He'll never let it go,' said another.

'Then we'll trick him,' said the third.

Two of the rogues continued to hide in the trees at the side of the road. The third one walked out of hiding and up to the man. 'Good morning,' he said. 'That's a fine dog you've got there. It looks like a good hunting dog.' And the rogue walked away, quickly down the road, and disappeared to rejoin his friends.

'Dog?' thought the man. 'The man must be a fool. Anyone can see that this is a goat, not a dog.' And he shrugged his shoulders and walked on.

The second rogue came out of his hiding place in the trees, and caught up with the man on the road.

'Hello,' he said. 'What are you doing? You look as though you're going to the village, but why are you walking along with that dog? The people will laugh at you. It's a silly looking animal.' And the rogue quickened his pace, hurried off down the road, and rejoined his friends under cover of the trees.

'That's funny,' thought the man. 'That's the second person who thinks I'm walking along with a dog, not a goat. Perhaps I've made a mistake.'

The man stopped and took a good look at the goat by his side. He stroked his back. He felt its head and its ears. He touched the beard on its chin, and felt its legs and feet. It certainly looked like a goat. It felt like a goat. Surely it was a goat.

'Yes,' he said to himself. 'Of course it's a goat.'

And he carried on walking down the road.

The first rogue left his friends and walked up to the man with the goat.

'Morning,' he said. 'Nice day isn't it? I hope you haven't far to go. The sun is going to be hot today, and that dog will be tired and thirsty before much longer. I should let it go if I were you. Let it go to find a stream for a drink of cool water. Poor thing.' And the rogue hurried away before the man had time to think of anything to say to him.

'Well!' said the man to the goat. 'It seems I am a fool. I thought you were a goat, but three different people have now told me you are a dog. Three separate people can't be wrong, can they? They must be right. I'll do what the last man said. I'll let you go, then you can find a drink of water. I don't want a dog anyway. It's a goat I wanted. Go on!' And he untied the soft rope from around the goat's neck, and let it loose.

The goat skipped and pranced down the road, and soon disappeared in the trees.

The man never saw it again. He never saw the three rogues again, either.

The man lost his goat to the three rogues. Just because three people told him the same thing, the man believed them. Yet his own common sense must have told him that the animal by his side was a goat.

I don't suppose anyone will try to trick you out of a goat, but they might try to tell you something that you know is not right. Stick to what you believe and don't let people make you change your mind!

Prayer

Dear God, help us to think for ourselves. Help us to listen to our conscience and do what we believe is the right thing to do. Help us to know that other people aren't necessarily right, even though there might be many people in agreement.

Amen

Hymn

'One more step' *Come and Praise* Vol 1

Biblical references to the theme

Week 3   Feelings

'Ruth answered, "You are very kind to me, sir. You have made me feel better by speaking gently to me." '

Ruth 2:13

'When my thoughts were bitter
and my feelings were hurt . . .
Yet I always stay close to you,
and you hold me by the hand.'

Psalms 73:21 and 23

'But now you must get rid of all these things: anger, passion, and hateful feelings.'

Colossians 3:8

The Jersey cow

Week 3   Feelings

Do you ever have a day when something happens that makes you feel bad-tempered, out of sorts, thoroughly cross and miserable? The trouble is, when you feel like that, it's quite difficult to feel normal again. When someone tries to help, you sometimes keep on feeling cross. It's an effort to stop feeling cross; but it's usually worth it.

In today's story, someone felt cross because she thought she wasn't needed any more, and she forgot about the things she was good at.

Jessie the Jersey cow was beautiful. She had a soft light brown coat, and lovely big brown eyes. She was friendly and the most placid cow on the farm. She was never bad tempered or cross, never kicked over her bucket of milk when the farmer was milking her, never nipped or kicked her calf, never in fact did anything wrong; until Tuesday of last week.

Jessie was the last of the Jerseys on Haighfield Farm. There used to be six of them, all alike, all with the same soft brown coats, but one by one they'd grown old and died. The farmer hadn't bought more. He'd decided to buy pigs instead. There were dozens of those. But, last Tuesday, he'd bought four more cows.

'There you are, Jess,' he said to her. 'Friends for you. You'll not be lonely any more.' And to her astonishment he opened the gate of her field and ushered in four big black and white Friesian cows.

Jessie stared at them with her huge brown eyes, and they stared back with their beady black ones. And that's when the trouble started.

She felt shy and uncomfortable under the gaze of the four pairs of eyes. She looked round at her pale brown coat and thought it looked drab next to their bright black and whites. She looked at her small brown calf and thought theirs would be much much bigger when they came. She looked at the bucket of creamy milk the farmer had collected that morning. No doubt the new cows would give at least two buckets each! Jessie felt miserable. Then she felt cross.

'I'm not having it,' she said. 'Everything was all right until they came. Well, I'm just not having it.' And she ran full tilt at the gate of the field. It fell over and Jessie ran out into the lane. She galloped down the lane with her calf running after her. She rounded the corner into the farmyard and suddenly found herself entangled with the farmer's wife's washing. She snorted and bellowed and stamped, and the washing was trampled into the mud under her hooves.

The farmer's wife came running out of the house to see what the commotion was, but as soon as the back door opened, Jessie ran into the kitchen. Her nose swept along the table and knocked five apple pies to the floor. A chair fell over and her tail swished two ornaments off the window-sill.

'Oh no you don't my lady!' said the farmer's wife, and she pushed Jessie back out of the door. Then she hugged her.

'Now, whatever is all this about?' she asked. 'Got out of bed on the wrong side this morning?'

Jessie hung her head and looked at the farmer's wife from under her long eyelashes.

The farmer's wife led Jessie back along the lane to the field, and all the time she talked to her.

'You have no need to worry about those Friesians, you know. They might be a bit younger than you, but they're not as beautiful. You've got a very special place on our farm. You give the best milk of any cow we've ever had. And you produce the prettiest babies. Where is your calf, by the way?'

By now they were back at the broken gate. The calf was walking along behind its mother, and Jessie was feeling much calmer and less cross than earlier.

'Now, you just stay there, while I mend this gate,' said the farmer's wife. Jessie stayed in the field. She made no attempt to escape again. After all, she was the most beautiful and most placid cow on the farm, everyone knew that.

When Jessie stopped to think about it, she knew that she had her own talents and abilities, and that she had nothing to fear from the new Friesians. They probably all ended up being the best of friends; I hope so.

Prayer
Help us Lord, to know that we each have something to feel good about. Help us to know that we are each good at something. Help us to be positive about our own ideas, background, talents and abilities.

Amen

Hymn
'Stand up, clap hands, shout thank you, Lord'   *Someone's singing, Lord*

The fair king
adapted from Islamic teaching

Week 3   Feelings

I'm sure you know what it feels like to be scared, or upset, or worried about something. It's not very pleasant, is it? And I know that some of you are very good about understanding when other people have those feelings. Some of you are very good at 'putting yourself in someone else's shoes'; that means looking at something from the other person's point of view. It's a very useful thing to be able to do; it helps you to be an understanding and kind sort of person. But sometimes, it's quite a difficult thing to do, especially if the other person is very different from you. In today's story, a king was able to put himself in the shoes of his people, and it helped him to be a more understanding king.

A man had just finished building himself a new house. It looked lovely. The man moved himself and all his possessions into the house, and sat back to enjoy the first night in his new home.

Suddenly it began to rain. To his horror, the man discovered that his beautiful new roof was leaking. He went outside, climbed up onto it and started to try to patch it. But, no matter what he did, the roof continued to leak. Inside the house, all his things were beginning to get wet, and the man knew that unless he could get help, everything would soon be spoiled by the water.

He went outside to try to find someone to help him, but the only person he could see was a man hurrying past the end of the road.

'Can you come and help me please,' he called, not really expecting the stranger to say yes; but he did. He went with the man to his house and started work straightaway. He worked for nearly four hours on the roof, and managed to fix the leak. When the water stopped pouring in, he helped the house-owner to dry everything out and put things back in their proper places.

By the time the two of them had finished, it was almost light; almost morning.

'I really am grateful to you,' said the house-owner. 'I don't know what I would have done without you. And now I must pay you for all your work.' He reached into his pocket, and was dismayed to find only a two pence coin there. He certainly couldn't pay the man two pence for all that hard work; it would be an insult.

'I'm ever so sorry,' said the house-owner, 'But this is all I have. Will you come back a little later this morning, when I've had time to go to the bank. Then I'll have some money and I'll be able to pay you.'

'No,' said the stranger. 'I'm afraid I can't possibly come back later. It really doesn't matter. I'll just take the two pence, and we'll call that it. I really don't want to be paid any more.'

'But you must,' said the house owner. 'I can't possibly pay you only two pence for all the hard work you've done. Please come back later and let me pay you some more.'

'No I can't,' said the man, and he looked anxiously at the daylight spreading across the sky. 'I really do have to go. And I must go now. I'll take the two pence.' And without any more ado, he took the two pence coin from the man whose house it was, and left.

Later that morning, the house owner collected some cash from the bank and began to search for the man who had helped him. He searched everywhere, in every neighbouring town and village. He asked people if they knew where he could find the man, but no-one seemed to know of him.

Fifteen years later, quite by chance, the house owner met the king. They began to talk together and the man was surprised at how understanding the king was. He seemed to be able to think like an ordinary man and to understand the problems of ordinary people. As he spoke, the king rolled a small coin between his fingers.

'Is the coin a special coin?' asked the man.

The king held it still, looked at it and said, 'Yes. I was given this coin once for helping to mend a roof. I have kept it safe ever since. You see, once or twice every week, I go out of the palace. I go in disguise, so that no-one will know who I am. I go to mix with my people so that I can understand what their lives are like. One night a man asked me to help him mend his roof, and he gave me this coin because he had no other money at the time. I'm glad I have the chance to be with my people. I'm glad I had the chance to do the job of an ordinary man.'

The story doesn't say whether the man told the king it was his roof he helped to mend, all those years before. I think the king learned a great deal, by doing a different job from the one he usually did. Everyone can learn a great deal by trying to see things from another person's point of view; by putting themselves in someone else's shoes; by trying to understand how the other person feels.

Prayer
Help us Lord, to see the other person's point of view. Help us to see the other side of things. Help us to be able to understand other people's feelings.

Amen

Hymn
'Think, think on these things' *Someone's singing, Lord*

The woman and the three loaves of bread   Week 3   Feelings
adapted from Jewish fable

Do you think you should do something kind for someone just to get a reward? No, I don't, either. I think it's best to do a kind deed for its own sake, rather than for what you might get out of it. But sometimes, kind deeds have been known to bring surprising results. They did in today's story. The ending was not at all what the old woman expected.

Once upon a time, an old woman lived all alone in a cottage by the side the sea. She had little money and few possessions, but she was a kind old lady and tried always to be helpful and cheerful.

She earned a living by mending the fishermen's nets. Each day when they came home to harbour after a shift at sea, some of their nets would be torn and damaged. The old woman mended them and earned a few pence for every net she repaired.

One winter, the weather was worse than usual. Storms raged and blew, and the sea was too angry for ships to set sail. The fishermen stayed home. Their nets stayed whole; and the old woman had no work. No work meant no pay. And no pay meant no food.

One day, the old woman had nothing left to eat in the house, and no money to buy bread. She scraped the bottom of the flour barrel and found just enough flour to make into dough. She mixed and kneaded, raised and baked, and soon had three golden brown crusty loaves. Delicious!

When they were cool, the old woman put one loaf on the table, and was just about to slice into it, when there was a knock on her door. Standing on her doorstep was a bedraggled beggar.

'Please can you spare something for me to eat?' said the man. 'I'm starving. I haven't eaten for days.'

'You do look hungry,' said the old woman. 'I know what hunger feels like. Here.' And she gave him the loaf of bread she had been going to eat.

'Thank you,' said the man.

The old woman went back into her kitchen and put the second of her loaves on the table. She was just about to slice into it when there was another knock at her door. The woman went to answer it. There on her doorstep stood a stranger, more bedraggled than the first man had been.

'Please can you help me,' said the man. 'I've been set upon by robbers. Everything I own has been stolen. I have no money for food; I have nothing. Could you please spare me something to eat?'

'I know how it feels to be in need,' said the old woman. 'Here, have this loaf of bread.' And she gave him the loaf of bread she had been going to eat.

'Thank you,' said the man.

The woman returned to her kitchen and put the third of her loaves on the table. She lifted her knife to cut a thick slice. She was really hungry by now. Suddenly a huge gust of wind buffeted the house. The woman's door burst open and the wind whistled inside. It flurried round the kitchen, displacing and dislodging things. It whipped the cloth off the table, and whisked the last loaf of bread high into the air. Then, as suddenly as it had come, it went, taking the loaf of bread with it.

'And what have I done to deserve that?' shouted the old woman. 'That's just not fair. I've given two of my loaves away to people whose need was greater than mine, and all I asked was that I be allowed to eat my very last loaf. But oh no! The wind has got it. And of what use is it to the wind?' And the old woman, who was usually so cheerful, sat down at her table and began to cry. But she was not downcast for long.

'I'll go and tell King Solomon,' she said. 'I'll go and complain about the wind.' So she did.

King Solomon listened carefully to what the old woman told him.

'I cannot decide what to do until I have heard the wind's side of the story,' he said. 'You'll have to wait here until this evening; until the wind can come.'

The old woman sat down to wait for the arrival of the wind. While she was waiting, three sailors came hurrying in to see the king. They were carrying a sack of gold.

'We must give this to someone who needs it,' they said. 'You can help us decide who that should be.'

'Why?' asked King Solomon.

'We were at sea and a dreadful storm blew up,' said the sailors. 'Our ship sprang a leak, and try as we might we knew we could not mend it. We were surely doomed to drown. We said if we reached land alive, we would give one tenth of our cargo of gold to a poor person in need. So here we are with a tenth of our gold. There's seven thousand gold pieces.'

'I don't understand,' said King Solomon. 'How are you here if you thought you were going to drown?'

'The strangest thing happened,' said the sailors. 'The wind blew something into the hole in the side of our ship. It sealed the hole until we could get to land. Look, this is what the wind brought.' The sailors unwrapped a wet and soggy loaf.

'Ah!' said King Solomon. 'I think I know about that.'

He turned to the old woman, 'Do you recognise this loaf?'

'Yes, it's mine. I baked it this morning,' she said.

'Then you can have it back!' said King Solomon. 'Oh, and by the way, you can have this as well.' And he gave her the sack of seven thousand gold pieces.

I don't suppose the old woman dreamed of a reward like that when she was helping the two men who came to her door. I think she helped them because she understood how they felt. I wonder what she did with the seven thousand pieces of gold. What do you think?

Prayer

Help us, Lord, to understand the feelings of others. Help us to be able to share what we have with others. Help us to do things out of kindness and not just for what we might be given.

Amen

Hymn

'Guess how I feel' *Come and Praise* Vol 2

Biblical references to the theme   *Week 4   Partners*

'For we are partners working together for God,'

1 Corinthians 3:9

'For we are all partners with Christ if we hold firmly to the end the confidence we had at the beginning.'

Hebrews 3:14

Rogationtide   *Week 4   Partners*
Rogation Sunday is the Sunday before Ascension Day, ie the fifth Sunday after Easter. The three Rogation Days are the days between Rogation Sunday and Ascension Day.

This is the time of year when we ask God to bless all the food we get from the earth, and to bless the people who work to produce our food. This time of year is called Rogationtide. It's a time when people think about being partners with God, in helping things to grow. People can prepare the ground and plant seeds, but without the rain and sun sent by God, the plants will not grow. God can send the sun and rain, but without people to sow the seeds and keep the weeds down, the plants will not grow well. So it's a partnership, between people and God.

Today's story is the legend of the first Rogationtide; the first partnership.

Luc lived nearly 1500 years ago, in a village near the mountains. It was his job to look after the land, and to try to grow food for the people of the village. Luc did his best, but he never managed to grow very much.

Whenever he remembered, he would plant a few cabbages, or carrots, or beans. Sometimes, he would plant a few grains of wheat, or he would put some potatoes in the ground. He used to say, 'God will do the rest. God will send the sun and the rain and he will make my plants grow.' And then Luc would sit back and wait for God to do his part of the work.

The trouble was that God didn't seem to be doing his bit. The plants never seemed to grow properly. There was never enough food for the people of the village, certainly in the winter-time; and more often than not, the people went hungry.

'You'll have to do better than this,' they said to Luc. 'After all, it's your job to grow the food for our village.'

'I can't help it if God isn't doing his job properly, can I?' said Luc. 'It's not my fault,' and he went on just as before, planting a few things here and there, and waiting to see what would grow.

One day a wise man came walking through the village. He looked at Luc's straggly beans and struggling cabbages. He saw the few poor thin stalks of wheat and the potato plants choked with weeds.

'Why is your land in such a mess?' he asked. 'Why don't you look after it properly?'

'I do,' said Luc. 'It's God who doesn't do his job properly. I plant the seeds and wait for them to grow. But they never do. Well, not properly. It's God's fault.'

'I don't think it is,' said the stranger. 'I think you've forgotten that you need to work *with* God. You and he need to be partners. You can't just leave him to it.'

'What do you mean?' asked Luc.

'Well,' said the wise man, 'God will send the rain and the sun, but *you* have to do some work too. *You* have to dig the ground and clear away the stones. *You* have to get rid of the weeds and pick off the caterpillars and slugs.'

'It sounds like hard work to me,' said Luc.

'It is,' said the wise man. 'But then nearly everything that's worth doing is hard work. Would you like me to help you? We'll ask all the other villagers to help too.'

'Yes please,' said Luc.

That evening, the wise man asked all the people of the village to meet together in one of the fields. He told them that they must all help, if they were to grow enough food for the whole village. He said that they must remember to work with God, and that God and people need to be partners.

The people listened quietly. Then they asked what they should do.

'First we must dig the earth,' said the wise man. 'Then we must plant the seeds. When we've done that, we must ask God to bless our work. Then we must look after the plants as they grow; we can't just leave it up to God.'

'We'll help,' said the people.

They started work immediately. They cleared the land of stones and rubbish. Then they dug the rich dark soil. They planted wheat seeds, for their bread, and vegetables to make their soup. When they had finished, they stood in the middle of the land and asked God to bless the work they had done.

'Dear God, please bless our work. Please help these plants to grow, so that in time we can use them for our food,' they said.

That year, the plants grew well and the people had plenty of food for the winter time.

Ever since then, at Rogationtide, many churches ask for God's blessing on all that is planted, and on the work that is done on the land.

Everything we do is a partnership; a partnership between us, other people, and God. When things don't work out quite as we planned, we need to check that we are doing our share of the partnership work, just as the wise man in the story advised Luc and the others to do.

Prayer
Dear God, please help us to work with you and with others as partners. Please bless the work of all the people who work on the land to produce our food.

Amen

Hymn
'We thank you Lord'   *Come and Praise* Vol 2

The maypole dancers   *Week 4   Partners*

Have you ever danced round a maypole? I know some of you have. Perhaps others of you have seen maypole dancing on television. A maypole is a large pole, usually decorated with painted stripes. It has 32 coloured ribbons fastened to the top of the pole, and 32 people each hold one of the ribbons. The people dance round the maypole, and as they dance, the ribbons weave into wonderful patterns. There are dances called plaits, and spirals, and spiders' webs. You can imagine the patterns the ribbons make, by the names of the dances.

No doubt you can also imagine that the people have to dance very carefully. They have to know what to do so that they don't get the ribbons tangled and knotted. They also have to know how to *un-dance* the ribbons, and weave the patterns out again.

Listen to what happened to the people in today's story.

The children and grown-ups of Nedboc Primary School decided to have a Spring Fair. It would be a fun day for everyone, they said, and at the same time it would raise funds for the school. All the important people who were in charge of Nedboc had long meetings together to make the plans.

They decided there would be stalls and games, sports and displays.
'The children could have a fancy dress parade,' someone said.
'The grown-ups could have a tug-of-war,' said someone else.
'And all the people who are in charge of Nedboc School could put on a maypole dancing display,' said yet someone else.
'Oh no!' said half the meeting.
'Oh yes, what a good idea,' said the other half.

And so it was that the headmistress and the teachers, the school governors and the man from the office in town, all had to learn how to dance round the maypole in time for the Nedboc School Spring Fair.

The day of the fair arrived. The sun shone, and everyone arrived at school early. The stalls were put up and the goods displayed. The rope arrived for the tug-of-war, and the maypole was brought out from the school hall and put up in the middle of the playing field. The children began to arrive in their fancy dress costumes. All was going well.

At two o'clock the Nedboc School Spring Fair was declared open. Now was the time for the maypole display. The music began and the headmistress, the teachers, the school governors and the man from the office in town all danced on to the field in a line. They took up their places round the maypole. Each had a ribbon to hold. The music changed and the first dance began. The dancers turned to face their partner and bow. And at that precise moment things started to go wrong.

You see, not one of them was happy with the partner they had. Instead of getting on with the job and doing their best, each person was determined not to help their partner. The headmistress trod on the toes of the caretaker. The man from the office in town deliberately pushed the deputy head. The chairman of governors dropped his ribbon and grabbed the cook's ribbon instead.

The music carried on playing.

The teacher of class two swapped places with the cleaning lady, and the dinner lady shouted at the cook, then dropped her ribbon and went home.

Some of the dancers tried to carry on. The music carried on playing.

Class four's teacher tripped up the teacher of class five, and the caretaker wrapped his ribbon round the teacher of class six.

The music carried on playing.

The dancers who were valiantly trying to keep to the dance and weave their ribbons in the right pattern, were beginning to get angry with the dancers who were spoiling it. Some of them gave up, threw their ribbons into the muddle in the middle, and walked off. Others decided to take matters into their own hands; they danced furiously round and round the muddle until they had tied everyone to the maypole with the ribbons.

The music continued.

Finally, the only two dancers left who still held ribbons and were not tied to the maypole, were the cook and the cleaning lady.

'Shall we?' asked the cook.

'Yes, let's,' said the cleaning lady. So they did. They tied the ends of all the ribbons together in one huge complicated knot, with many of the dancers still trapped between the ribbons and the maypole. Then they pushed the maypole over. It landed with a crash on the ground.

Suddenly, all the spectators who had been standing laughing at the ridiculous spectacle, leapt into action. Things were, after all, becoming nasty and dangerous now. What had been just plain silly, was now serious. Someone might be hurt.

Scissors were brought. The beautiful coloured ribbons had to be cut away. The dancers were released from the maypole. The maypole was righted again. It looked in a sorry state. It was badly damaged. It's cut and torn ribbons hung limply in tattered shreds. The dancers looked dreadful. Their clothes were torn and their arms and legs were bruised and scratched, but luckily no-one was seriously hurt. The dancers were led away to the school building for first aid and cups of tea.

The Nedboc School Spring Fair was declared closed, everything was cleared away and the people all went home.

The next day the headmistress and the staff, the governors and the man from the office in town all apologized to the whole school for their disgraceful behaviour.

Nedboc school never again had a Spring Fair.

And it was all because people would not work as partners with other people!

I'm glad the grown-ups at our school are not as silly as the people of Nedboc School. And I'm glad that *you* know how to work with a partner when you need to. You don't have to *like* everyone in the world; but must try to get along with them.

Prayer
Help us Lord, to get along with other people. Help us to know that there are times when we must work with other people as partners. Help us to see the other person's point of view and help us not to be selfish.

Amen

Hymn
'Hevenu shalom'   *Alleluya*

A cow, a lioness and a jackal
adapted from the Sandhibheda-Jātaka

Week 4   *Partners*

I wonder how many different partners you have in a day? You might have a partner you come to school with, or one you line up with. You'll probably have a partner to sit next to or to work with. Most of you have a special partner – a best friend – who you like to be with in your spare time.

Partners need looking after. Partners need to be cared for. But sometimes other people might try to break up a friendship or spoil a partnership. Then you have to decide who to be loyal to. I hope you would choose to be loyal to your friend.
Someone tried to break up a friendship in today's story.

A cow was once accidentally left behind by a cowherd who was supposed to be looking after the whole herd. He'd taken the herd to another part of the forest and he thought he had all the cows with him. When the cow realised that the other cows had gone, she knew there was little she could do. She didn't know where they had gone, and she couldn't go looking for them because she knew that very soon her baby calf would be born. So she stayed where she was.
Living in that part of the forest was a lioness. She'd been watching the herd of cows, and wondered whether she could manage to catch one to eat, but she'd given up the idea because she too was having a baby, and she knew she could not run very fast just now.
The cow and the lioness met. Quite extraordinarily, they became friends. The calf and the lion cub were born, and the two mothers helped each other with the babies.
A man who lived in the forest, went to tell the king about the unusual friendship between the cow and the lioness.
'They're the best of friends,' he said. 'They don't fight or argue, and never once have I seen the lioness try to attack the cow. Isn't it strange!'
'No,' said the king. 'There are unusual friendships between animals who are usually enemies. The thing to watch, is that a third animal doesn't try to break the friendship. Keep your eyes open and come and tell me if you see another animal with them.'
'I will,' said the forester, and he went back to the wood to watch.
It wasn't long before he noticed a jackal stalking the two friends. The forester watched. The jackal seemed to be waiting until he saw each animal alone, then he appeared to be speaking to it. The curious thing, though, was that he never spoke to the cow and the lioness together. He only spoke to them individually. The forester watched and listened.
'Do you know what that lioness calls you behind your back?' the jackal whispered to the cow one day.
'She doesn't say nasty things about me,' said the cow. 'She's my friend.'
'She's not really your friend,' said the jackal. 'She says you're mean and that you don't look after your baby properly.'
The cow was very hurt to think that the lioness had been saying such things about her. Of course, the truth was that the lioness has said no such thing. The jackal was making it up to make trouble between the friends.

Later, the jackal spoke to the lioness.

'That cow has been gossiping about you to others in the forest,' he said.

'I'm sure she hasn't,' said the lioness. 'She and I are good friends. We don't say nasty things about each other.'

'That's what you think,' said the jackal. 'She says you are not fit to be the mother of your cub. And she called you unrepeatable names.'

'Did she?' said the lioness.

'She did. I'm telling you the truth,' said the jackal.

But of course, the jackal was not telling the truth. He was merely trying to stir up trouble between the friends.

The sad thing was, his plan worked. The two friends believed what the jackal had said. They each thought that the other had been disloyal. They each decided to get their own back.

The very next day a terrible fight broke out between the lioness and the cow. The calf and the cub joined in, and the fight was so fierce that all four were near death by the time the forester ran to tell the king of the dreadful event.

The king and the forester came hurrying back to the scene of the fight.

Four animals lay dead on the bare earth.

The only sign of life was a jackal running away in the hope that the king would not see him.

'Oh dear!' sighed the king. 'This is what happens when people listen to evil words from others. This is what happens when people take notice of scandal-mongers and trouble-makers. Oh dear! And they were such good friends. If they'd taken no notice of the jackal, or at least if they'd checked the facts, they'd have still been alive now. Oh dear!'

And the king walked sadly away.

It's not a very happy ending, is it? I hope you won't take any notice if anyone says nasty things about one of your friends. Or at least, check whether what they say is true or not, before you act on what they say. And I know that no-one here would spread lies about someone, like the jackal in the story.

Prayer

Thank God, for our friends. Help us to look after our friends; to care for them; to be loyal to them; to speak up for them. Help us to remember never to tell lies to, or about, our friends. Help us to work well with the different partners we have throughout the day. Help us to remember that we are all partners in our world family.

Amen

Hymn
'If I had a hammer'   *Come and Praise* Vol 1

Biblical references to the theme
Week 5   Sharing

'Be generous and share your food with the poor. You will be blessed for it.'

Proverbs 22:9

'Whoever shares with others should do it generously:'

Romans 12:8

'Command them to do good, to be rich in good works, to be generous and ready to share with others.'

1 Timothy 6:18

The three fish
Week 5   Sharing

adapted from Indian fable

I like to think that everyone in our school is good at sharing. I know we have people who are good at sharing books and equipment in the classrooms, and people are kind enough to share their own things with their friends. I think we would have a very unhappy school if we didn't share; if we were all selfish and tried to keep everything to ourselves.

In today's story a man and his wife couldn't agree about sharing some fish. I wonder how *you* would have solved the problem.

A man went out shopping to buy some fish for tea for himself and his wife. He looked at the fish on the market slab and wondered which to buy. A huge flat fish? No, too big. Some tiny sardines? No, too small. But there, in the middle of the slab, were three middle-sized-silvery-white-fine-fat-fish.

'Just right for me and my wife,' he said and he bought them.

He carried them carefully home and put them on the kitchen table.

'You've shopped well,' said his wife. 'Three fine fish and they look delicious, but why have you only bought one for yourself? I see you have bought two for me!'

'No,' said the man. 'I bought one for you. The other two are for me.'

'But that's not fair,' said his wife. 'I want two!'

'Well, you're only having one,' said her husband. 'Because I'm having two!'

'But I should have two because I'm going to cook them,' she said.

'So what?' he shouted. 'I went and bought them, so I should have two.'
'If you loved me you'd let me have two,' she wheedled.
'If you respected me you'd want me to have two,' he grumbled.
'Well, I don't think it's fair,' she shouted.
'Neither do I,' he yelled.
'I'm never going to speak to you again,' she cried.
'Well that suits me,' he said. 'In fact, I'm not going to speak to you either. I'm going to leave those three fine fat fish in the middle of the table, and whichever one of us speaks first can have one, and the other can eat two. That'll settle it.'
'Right!'
And then after all that noise . . . silence. Neither of them spoke a word. They sat, one at each side of the kitchen table with the three fine fat fish between them. They didn't speak. They didn't move. They just sat. Quite still. Soundless.
The neighbours had heard the shouting and commotion as the man and his wife argued over the fish. They came out of their houses to listen and to laugh.
'They're at it again,' someone said.
'What are they arguing about this time?' asked another.
'Something to do with some fish,' said a third.
'It's all gone quiet now,' said someone else. 'Do you think they're all right?'
'They will be,' said the first neighbour. 'They're always arguing. They'll start again in a minute.'
But they didn't start again in a minute. They didn't even start again in an hour.
'They're awfully quiet aren't they?' someone said.
'Perhaps we ought to go and see if they're all right.'
'Perhaps we should. Perhaps they're dead!'
At the thought of the man and his wife having killed each other in the argument, all the neighbours hurried round to the house. They looked in through the open door. They saw the man and his wife sitting at each side of the kitchen table, and the three fine fat fish between them.
'Are you all right?' they called in through the door.
No answer.
'Are you both all right?' they called, a little louder.
Still no answer.
'I think they really are dead,' said someone. 'Go in and pinch them and see if they're still breathing. Go on,' and the neighbours pushed one of the women in through the door.
She walked right up to the silent man and pinched him hard on his arm.

'Ow! That hurt!' he said.

As soon as he opened his mouth to speak, his wife jumped up from her chair and said 'They're mine! The fish are mine!'

She grabbed two fish from the middle of the table, flung them into a frying pan, and cooked them golden brown.

Then she ate them.

The man and his wife were not very good at sharing, were they? I wonder if you think she should have had the two fish, or whether you think her husband should have had two? Or perhaps you would have shared the fish differently. What would you have done?

Prayer
Dear God, please help us not to be selfish. Help us to share what we have with our family and friends. Help us to share our world with all the people in it.   *Amen*

Hymn
'Let there be peace on earth'   *Alleluya*

The last leaf
adapted from a story by O'Henry   *Week 5   Sharing*

If I say the word 'sharing' to you, I wonder what you think of: sharing toys and games perhaps, or sharing a bag of crisps with a friend? It's good to share things with our friends and family. But have you thought that you can also share your talents and your time? These are much harder to share than possessions and often take a bit more thought. Today's story is about someone who shared his talent. The man was a painter and he used his painting skill to help a neighbour.

Sue and Joanna were artists. They shared a studio in New York, in a part where lots of artists lived. The studio was small and cold and was at the top of a three-storey house, but the north light from the attic windows was just right for painting. With a north light, the artists could mix their colours perfectly.

At first all went well. It was summer and the attic studio was cool. Sue and Joanna sold a few pictures and earned enough money to buy food and more painting materials.

And then the winter came, bringing cold damp weather. The studio became chilled and uncomfortable, and Joanna became ill.

'You'll be better soon,' said Sue. But Joanna's illness grew worse. She had pneumonia and the doctor said she might not live.

'Come on,' said Sue to her. 'Don't give up. You must fight this disease. Then you'll be well again.'

'No,' said Joanna. 'I'm going to die. I know I am.' She turned her face to the window and looked outside. 'Do you see that tree?' she said.

Sue looked and saw the tree Joanna meant. It was an old gnarled climbing plant growing against the wall of the house opposite. It had a few straggly leaves still clinging on to it.

'What about it?' asked Sue.

'Each day, more of those leaves fall off that tree. When the last leaf falls, I'm going to die,' said Joanna.

'What rubbish!' said Sue. 'I'm not going to listen to this miserable talk,' and she went away to make some soup for dinner. Later, she went out and spoke to Mr Behrman, the old painter who lived downstairs.

The next day was wet and windy with snow in the air. There were only four leaves left on the tree.

'I think they'll all be gone by tomorrow,' said Joanna. 'Tomorrow.' And she sighed.

During that night the wind and rain beat against the windows.

'Those last few leaves will not withstand this storm,' thought Sue. 'They'll all be blown off the tree by the morning, and as soon as Joanna sees them gone, she'll just give up. I know she will.'

In the morning the wind was still blowing strongly and Sue hardly dared to pull back the curtains. She was sure that all the leaves would be gone. But no. One was left. One lone leaf hung, bravely and stiffly, on the branch.

The storm continued, but the next day the single leaf was still there. And the next day. And the next.

Joanna began to feel a little stronger.

'If that leaf can hang on to the tree throughout the storm, I can hang on to life,' she said. 'I must not give up hope.'

Each day Joanna grew a little better and a little stronger, and the leaf stayed on the tree.

The doctor came to see her again.

'You're much better,' he said. 'Over the worst now. You'll live. But your neighbour is ill, did you know? Mr Behrman, the painter from downstairs. He's in hospital.'

'I hope he gets well soon,' said Joanna.

A week later Joanna was almost well again, and the solitary leaf was still on the tree.

'I have something to tell you,' said Sue to Joanna. 'Mr Behrman died today. You knew he was in hospital?'

'Yes,' said Joanna.

'Well, just over a week ago he was out painting at night in the middle of that dreadful storm. He became very ill with pneumonia.'

'What was he doing, painting outside, in the middle of the night?' asked Joanna.

'He was up a ladder, painting a beautiful leaf on the wall opposite your window. Look.' Sue pointed to the last single solitary leaf, still clinging to the climbing plant outside Joanna's window.

'He painted it for me,' said Joanna. 'To keep me alive. He painted a masterpiece for me.'

Mr Behrman had always wanted to paint a masterpiece – a best picture. His last picture, the leaf, was his best because he used all his skill to paint a leaf so life-like that Joanna would believe it was real.

Prayer

Thank you God, for our talents. Help us to remember that everyone is good at something. Help us to use our talents and our skills to help other people. Help us to share what we have with others.

Amen

Hymn

'Magic Penny' *Alleluya*

Mrs Robinson and Mrs Clegg

Week 5 Sharing

One of the most difficult things to share is our time. And yet it's one of the most precious things we can share. If we give someone some of our time, it's like giving them part of ourselves. Today's story is about two ladies in hospital. They had their birthdays on the same day and they were both given birthday presents by their families. I wonder what *you* think about what they were given?

Mrs Robinson and Mrs Clegg were getting along very well together. They hadn't known each other long, just since they'd come into hospital a week ago, but already they had lots of things in common. For instance, they both had two grandchildren, they both liked knitting and the same kind of chocolate biscuits, and then they found out that both their birthdays were on the very next day.

'We'll have a party,' said one of the nurses. 'Are your families coming to see you?'

'I think so,' said both ladies.

The next morning a nurse brought a bundle of cards for each of them. 'The postman's here,' she said. 'You've both got lots of cards.'

Mrs Robinson and Mrs Clegg opened the envelopes and showed each other their birthday cards. Mrs Robinson had one card that was absolutely enormous.

'It's from my grandchildren,' she said. 'They must have chosen the biggest card in the shop!'

'Look,' said Mrs Clegg, and she showed Mrs Robinson two tiny cards. 'These are from *my* grandchildren. They've made them for me. I can tell which is which without reading their names inside. This one with the drawing of the dog is from Tom; he loves dogs. And this one's Jenna's. She likes making things. Look, she's cut out all these flowers separately, and stuck them on.'

'They're lovely cards,' said Mrs Robinson. 'They must have taken a long time to make.'

'And your grandchildren must have spent all their pocket money on your card,' said Mrs Clegg. And both ladies smiled as they thought of their grandchildren.

Later that afternoon, the families of the people in the ward arrived for visiting time. Mrs Robinson's family hurried in with a huge bouquet of flowers arranged in a beautiful basket. It had ribbons on it and a card tucked inside which said Happy Birthday. There was also a big box of chocolates for her.

'Oh thank you,' said Mrs Robinson. 'What a lovely present. Come and sit down and you can help me eat my chocolates.'

'No, we can't stay long,' said her son. 'We just popped in to say Hello. We have to go again now because we're going out with our friends. We just wanted to wish you a Happy Birthday. 'Bye then. Have a nice day.' And they hurried away again.

''Bye,' said Mrs Robinson.

Just then, Mrs Clegg's family arrived. They said Happy Birthday to her, then they sat down to talk.

'We've brought you some flowers,' said Mrs Clegg's son. 'It's just a bunch from the garden. We picked them for you as we set off, so they're nice and fresh.'

'And I baked you a cake this morning,' said her daughter-in-law. 'It's chocolate – your favourite.'

'Oh thank you,' said Mrs Clegg. 'We'll all have a piece now. You must cut a piece for Mrs Robinson. It's her birthday as well, today.'

'We know,' said Jenna. 'This is for you.' And she gave a tiny present to Mrs Robinson. It was a lovely scented soap.

'I've brought some of my games to play,' said Tom. 'We can play them together and it'll be like a party.'

'And look Gran,' said Jenna. 'I've made you a bookmark. It's to save your place when you're reading.'

A nurse came by then, and cut the birthday cake. She gave everyone a slice. All the people on the ward sang Happy Birthday, and the two ladies agreed that it had indeed been a very happy birthday for each of them.

I wonder what *you* think of Mrs Robinson's and Mrs Clegg's birthday. Do you think one of them enjoyed her birthday more than the other? The two families were very different, weren't they?

Sometimes it's difficult to share our time, but it's good to try to do it, to show people we care.

Prayer
Dear God, help us please to share our time. Help us to know that when we give our time, we are giving a little bit of ourselves. Help us to show people that we care about them.

Amen

Hymn
'When I needed a neighbour' *Someone's singing, Lord*

Biblical references to the theme *Week 6 Whitsuntide*

The Whitsuntide story can be found in *Acts 2:1-42*

The first Whit Sunday *Week 6 Whitsuntide*

Did you know that Whitsuntide is the third most important Christian festival after Christmas and Easter? It always comes exactly 50 days after Easter. It marks the day on which Christians believe God sent the Holy Spirit to Jesus's friends. Jesus had already left his disciples and returned to his father in Heaven, but he promised his friends that he would send the Holy Spirit to help them be strong and brave enough to do his work.

There were crowds of people in Jerusalem. They had come to celebrate the Feast of Pentecost; to thank God for the harvest. The temples were decorated with fruit and flowers, and people crowded to the special thanksgiving services.

Jesus's disciples, Peter, James, John and the others, were in Jerusalem for Pentecost. Early in the morning they were together in an upstairs room. They had been talking together, and praying, when suddenly a fierce wind blew through the room.

The weather outside was still and calm; the wind seemed to be inside the room itself. The friends were afraid.

Then, as suddenly as the wind had started, it stopped, and there appeared, above the head of each man, a beautiful, bright flame of fire. The fire didn't touch them or burn them; it hovered, still and quiet, above each one. And then they understood. God had sent this message to show them that his Holy Spirit would make them strong and brave. Strong and brave enough to go out and tell the world about Jesus.

Peter said, 'Let's go now. There are crowds of people here, let's go and tell them what's happened.'

The friends agreed and together they went out of the upstairs room, onto a balcony. From here they could see the people in the street below. Peter went to the edge of the balcony and called down.

'Listen,' he said. A small group of people looked up and listened to what he had to say. Peter told them about Jesus. He told them that Jesus was a good man, but that he'd been killed. He told them about Jesus being alive on Easter Day, and how some of the disciples had seen him. He told them about Jesus going back to his father in Heaven, and sending the Holy Spirit as he promised he would.

By now there was a huge gathering of people under the balcony, listening to Peter's words. A few days ago Peter would have felt afraid, speaking to such a large number of people, but now he felt no fear, only a determination to tell all these people about Jesus.

And the strange thing was, that even though some of them were from different countries, and spoke different languages, every one of them could understand what Peter was saying.

Some of the people who had watched Jesus being killed on Good Friday were ashamed of what they had done.

'What can we do to put things right?' they asked.

'Tell God that you are sorry,' said Peter. 'And come and be baptised, then you too will receive the gift of the Holy Spirit.'

Later that day, and during the days that followed, Peter, James, John and the others taught and baptised no less than three thousand people.

On that first Whitsuntide, Peter taught people about Jesus for the first time. Whitsuntide is often called the birthday of the Christian church.

Prayer
Help us God, to be brave. Help us to do what we believe is right. Help us to be strong enough to listen to the voice of our conscience.

Amen

Hymn
'Who can see the great wind blow?' *Someone's singing, Lord*

The packman   *Week 6   Whitsuntide*

Christians believe that at Whitsuntide the Holy Spirit came to the disciples of Jesus to help them to be brave and strong. They believe that the Holy Spirit is in everyone, helping them to do what is right. In today's story a man had a good idea which helped him. Perhaps the good idea came from God.

The man was a packman; a person who carries goods from place to place to sell them. This man carried books – bibles mainly – and he carried them in a pack on his back. He had no horse or donkey, and it was in the days before cars or vans. The man was travelling in Italy, walking from town to village, and from village to city, selling his books where he could.

On this particular day he had sold very little. He had spent the day in a market place in a mountain village, and was trying to reach the next village before nightfall. He doubted that he would make it. The road was steep and not very well made, and the way was long.

The sky suddenly grew dark. Night came quickly in the mountains. The packman began to feel afraid. Perhaps he would lose his way and fall down the hillside. Perhaps there were wild animals that would eat him. Perhaps there were bandits who would attack him.

No sooner had fear taken hold of the man, than he heard the sound of hooves. A horseman rode fast past, then turned and faced him.

'Where've you been?' demanded the rider.

'To the market back there,' answered the packman.

'Then hand over your money,' growled the rider. 'Give me your takings or I'll kill you.'

The packman felt in his pocket for the few coins he had, and handed them over.

The robber spat on them and threw them to the ground.

'Are you trying to make a fool of me?' he shouted. 'Where's the rest?'

'I haven't any more,' said the packman.

'Then I'll take what's in your pack,' said the robber, and he snatched the bag from the packman and tipped out its contents onto the ground.

'Books!' he snarled. 'Waste of time!' And he began to rip apart the books and scatter their pages to the wind.

The packman knew there was nothing he could do. He couldn't escape. He would probably be killed by this robber. What a pity he didn't have any more money. If he'd been able to hand over gold and silver, perhaps the bandit would have taken it then left him alone.

Suddenly he had an idea. He picked up one of the torn bibles.

'Do you like stories?' he said, and before the robber could answer, the packman turned to the story of the Good Samaritan and started to read, 'There was once a man travelling from Jerusalem to Jericho when he fell among thieves.'

It was a good thing the packman knew the story by heart, because it was now too dark to see to read. But the robber seemed not to notice. The packman carried on with the story, ' "The robbers left him for dead by the side of the road. A Samaritan came by and helped the man. He bathed his wounds, then put him on his own donkey and took him to the nearest inn where he could be cared for." '

The robber looked at the packman. The packman wondered whether he would be angry with him, for telling that particular story.

But suddenly the robber picked up one of the bibles that littered the ground. 'I'll have this,' he said, and he rode off, leaving the packman standing alone.

After a few minutes, the packman gathered up all his books, stuffed them into his bag, and hurried off down the road. As he went, he said a silent prayer of thanks for the idea which had saved his life, for he knew without a doubt, that it was the bible story that had saved him.

Many, many years later, the packman met the robber again, quite by chance, but this time in a busy market town. And this time the robber didn't try to steal anything from the packman. Instead, he shook his hand and said, 'Thank you. You made me think, that night I met you on the road. I gave up my life of crime and now I'm a farmer. And look, I still have this. Let me pay you for it.' And he pulled out of his pocket the bible he had picked up from the road, all those years before.

'No,' said the packman. 'It's yours. I don't want you to pay me for it. It's payment enough to hear you've changed your way of life.'

The packman's good idea to read a story from the bible, helped not only himself, but the robber as well. And the packman was very strong and brave to forgive the robber.

Prayer
Dear God, help us to be brave when faced with difficulties. Help us to do what is right, and to turn away from what is wrong.

Amen

Hymn
'The journey of life' *Come and Praise* Vol 1

The Whitsuntide clothes

Week 6 Whitsuntide

Think of the last new clothes you had! You might have had a new T shirt, or a new jumper very recently. I know that the children in my family seem always to be getting new clothes. But it wasn't like that for children living in the north of England a few years ago.

The children had new summer clothes only at Whitsuntide. Their parents bought, or made, the new clothes and saved them until Whit Sunday. There was usually something white in the clothing because 'Whitsun' means 'White Sunday'.

Mrs Brown had been busy for weeks. Her sewing machine and knitting needles had hardly stopped, but now the two piles of clothes were nearly ready. Top-to-toe new clothes for Whitsuntide for each of her children. For Valerie, a dress, a cardigan, a new coat, new shoes and socks, a nightie and underwear. For John, his first long trousers, a jumper, a jacket, a shirt and tie, new shoes and socks, underwear and pyjamas.

The new clothes, of course, would only be 'for best'; they wouldn't be for school or playing out in. Mrs Brown, like all the mothers, was very strict about that. The new clothes would be for Sundays only.

'I can't *wait* for Sunday,' said Valerie. 'I bet I get more money than last year.'

'And I bet I get more money than *you*,' said John.

'Stop being so greedy, you two,' said Mrs Brown. 'There's more to Whitsuntide than getting money.' But John and Valerie just smiled.

At last Whit Sunday arrived. The children were not allowed to put on their new clothes until after breakfast. But then, what a to-do! All the children came out of their houses dressed beautifully. They went into each other's houses to show their new clothes. They called in to the houses of their relatives and neighbours. They twirled and paraded, spread skirts and opened jackets. In short, they showed off!

In every house there were exclamations:

'Well don't you look smart.'

'You do look grand.'
'What beautiful Whitsy clothes.'
And in every house visited, a coin was given to each child; a penny or two, or a shiny silver sixpence. The children visited as many houses as they were allowed!

Afterwards, with coins jingling in their pockets, they turned home again to collect their parents to go to church to say thank you for Whit Sunday.

After church the children gathered behind the band and the parade set off. Through the streets and round the houses they went, the band booming and the children marching. Everyone in the whole of the town came out to watch. Such excitement!

'I like Whitsuntide,' said Valerie. 'But I can't *wait* 'till this afternoon.'

Mrs Brown laughed at her. 'This afternoon will be here soon enough. But remember, keep clean!'

It was the same in all the houses; children wanting the afternoon party to begin, but mothers anxious about the beautiful new clean clothes.

The tea was set out on the spare land by the pond. Long tables laden with cakes and buns, jellies and tarts. The children played on the grass, but there were constant shouts from the mothers:

'Keep clean!'

'Don't get that dress dirty.'

'Don't sit on the grass in those trousers.'

Valerie and her friend threw stones into the pond.

'Don't get splashed,' called her mother.

Valerie threw another stone, but this time, somehow, she forgot to let go. The stone, Valerie, new dress, and all, fell into the muddy pond.

There was silence on the spare land by the pond. Then sudden pandemonium.

Valerie was fished out, the mothers fussed, the fathers tried to calm everyone. Someone produced a towel. She was dried. She cried.

Mrs Brown, as you can imagine, was extremely angry, and marched Valerie home. But the other mothers followed.

'It doesn't matter,' they said.

'Don't worry.'

'Change her into her old clothes and let her come back to the party.'

So Valerie, changed into her second best clothes for the rest of the party, came back. Luckily, Mrs Brown soon lost her anger, and Valerie and everyone else had a Whit Sunday no-one ever forgot.

Whitsuntide was a very special holiday for those children. Nowadays, our nearest holiday to Whitsuntide is Spring Bank Holiday, but you can work out when Whit Sunday is; it is always seven weeks after Easter Day.

Prayer
Thank you God, for Whitsuntide. Thank you for holidays and special days. Thank you for parties and celebrations. Thank you for new clothes.

Amen

Hymn
'Thank you Lord' *Come and Praise* Vol 1

Biblical reference to the theme

Week 7   Problems

'I tried to think this problem through, but it was too difficult for me until I went into your Temple.'

Psalms 73:16

'These proverbs can even add to the knowledge of wise men and give guidance to the educated, so that they can understand the hidden meanings of proverbs and the problems that wise men raise.'

Proverbs 1:5-6

Monsieur Jean's carnations

Week 7   Problems

I once knew a boy who made a really good picture. It was of a rocket. He'd used gold and silver felt pens, and he'd stuck on some sparkly tinsel to show the flames at the base of the rocket. He'd painted a thick black jagged edge to the picture to represent the darkness of space. Everyone said how good the picture was. And that was the trouble. After that, every time the boy made a picture, he tried to use the same idea because it had worked well the first time. But none of the pictures was as good as the first, and at last the boy learned that every problem has a different solution. You can't come along with the same answer every time you do something; it just doesn't work. The man in today's story didn't know this though.

Monsieur Jean was a farmer in France. He had a small farm high in the hills of a place called Provence and he grew flowers – beautiful carnations in every colour you could think of. He worked hard, especially in the summer time when the sun shone and the air was dry and warm and the plants needed watering twice every day.

Twice every week Monsieur Jean had to walk up and down the rows of carnations very early in the morning to pick the flowers that were ready. These he tied into bunches of ten, then he piled them on the donkey cart on wet sacks to keep them fresh. Then he set off down the hillside to sell the carnations at the market in the town. When they were all sold he would set off again, this time up the hillside to the farm, to get back in time for watering the plants in the evening.

One summer when the carnations were just beginning to flower, Monsieur Jean noticed that lots of the plants had been nibbled. The tender growing shoots had been bitten from the stems and the flower buds had been eaten.

Rabbits! Thought Monsieur Jean.

He hurried to see his neighbour who grew vegetables.

'It's the same on my farm,' said the neighbour, 'I've never known so many rabbits. We'll lose all the crops if we're not careful.'

'What shall we do?' asked Monsieur Jean.

'Buy some wire netting and some wooden posts,' said the neighbour, 'And build a fence round your flower field. That should do it.'

Monsieur Jean hurried to town to buy what he needed to build a rabbit-proof fence. He worked all night until the fence was finished. Then he watered the plants, picked the undamaged flowers, took them to market, came back and watered the plants again; and waited.

That night the rabbits came and pushed their soft noses against the wire netting fence. They stood on their hind legs and looked at the juicy plants through the patterned holes in the fence, but they couldn't reach them. Monsieur Jean's carnations were safe.

A few weeks after the new fence had been built, Monsieur Jean's carnations began to droop and wilt. The flower heads dropped off and the leaves turned yellow. Now the reason for this was that the flowers were not getting enough water. There was a stream running through Monsieur Jean's farm and he used water from this to water the flowers. But the stream had become blocked further up the hillside, and the water was running down a different channel. Monsieur Jean had not noticed that each day the stream was a little shallower, and each day he was giving the flowers fewer buckets of water.

He looked at the dying carnations.

'I know what to do,' he said suddenly. 'It worked last time.' And he hurried off to town to buy some more wire netting.

Monsieur Jean worked all through the night to put a new layer of wire netting on the fence. 'There! That should do it,' he said when he'd finished. But of course, this time the new fence didn't make any difference at all. A new fence might stop rabbits, but it doesn't make any difference to a blocked up stream!

The next day the neighbour came to Monsieur Jean's farm.

'The stream's blocked up,' he said, 'further up the hillside. Didn't you know?'

'No,' said Monsieur Jean.
'Well, don't worry, we're going up to unblock it. You stay here. Shout up and let us know when the water starts running again.'
'All right,' said Monsieur Jean.
The men climbed the hillside and started to clear the stones that were blocking the stream. Soon the water was running in Monsieur Jean's stream again, but still the men worked. More and more stones and debris were moved and the water began to flow much more strongly and quickly than ever it had before. The men carried on working. By now the stream was a raging torrent and it was overflowing its banks and flooding in to the carnation field.
'Stop!' shouted Monsieur Jean, but the men couldn't hear him above the sound of the rushing water.
'Never mind,' said Monsieur Jean to himself. 'I know what to do.' He ran to get a spare roll of wire netting, and standing up to his knees in water in the carnation field, he began to put a third layer of wire netting on the fence.
'That should do it!'
He worked as hard and as quickly as he could, but of course it didn't make any difference. A new fence might stop rabbits, but it doesn't make any difference to a flood! Soon Monsieur Jean's carnations were all washed away. Some of them were trapped against the wire netting fence, and I'm pleased to say he was able to take some cuttings and start all over again when the stream problem was sorted out.

It was a pity Monsieur Jean didn't know that every problem needs a different solution. He might have been able to save his field of carnations if he'd not tried to do the same thing every time there was a problem.

Prayer
Dear God, please help us to think. If we have a problem, help us to think sensibly and clearly so that we can find the best answer. Help us to know that other people might be able to help us, and we might be able to help them if they have a problem. Help us to work together.

Amen

Hymn
'It's a new day' *Come and Praise* Vol 2

Nasrudin and the donkeys
adapted from Islamic teaching

Sometimes you can search and search for the answer to a problem, only to find that it was under your nose all the time. But sometimes you can't see something that's staring you in the face. That happened to one of the men in today's story.

Nasrudin was a trader. He travelled all over the countryside buying and selling different things. He would buy and sell cloth, or fruit, or vegetables, or baskets, or anything that he thought people would find useful and would want to buy.

One of the roads that he travelled quite often, took him over the hills into a neighbouring country. And here he had to be careful. Here was a border guard who searched anyone travelling into or out of the country. People were able to take most things across the border, but there was a long list of things that were not allowed to be traded from one country to the next.

For several days now, Nasrudin had travelled the road over the hill. On each occasion the border guard had stopped him and questioned him, and on each occasion Nasrudin had told him politely that he was not taking anything across the border that he shouldn't have been taking.

But the border guard was suspicious. He believed Nasrudin was smuggling something across the border.

'I'll catch him out,' said the border guard. 'He won't fool me. I'll find what it is he's smuggling.'

The next day Nasrudin appeared on the road as usual. He was walking beside his donkey which had two panniers fastened to its saddle.

'Now then Nasrudin,' said the guard. 'I'll have to search you today. What have you got in those baskets?' And he began to rummage in the donkey's panniers to see what Nasrudin had hidden there. But he found nothing except some bundles of straw. He's smuggling something, he said to himself.

Later that same day, Nasrudin came back along the road, this time without his donkey.

'Come here,' said the guard. 'Turn out your pockets. I know you've got something hidden.' Nasrudin turned out his pockets, but the border guard found nothing except an old handkerchief and a bit of fluff. He's smuggling something, he said to himself.

The next morning Nasrudin appeared again on the road leading over the hill. Again the guard searched the donkey's saddle bags and Nasrudin's pockets.

'I want to look in your mouth and in your nose and in your ears,' said the guard. 'Perhaps you've hidden something tiny like diamonds and jewels in places you think I won't look!' But the border guard found nothing except an old filling that had fallen out of one of Nasrudin's teeth.

Later that day when Nasrudin came back on the road again alone, the border guard searched him once more, but found nothing. He's smuggling something, he said to himself.

And so it went on. Every day. Morning and evening. Nasrudin travelled backwards and forwards between the two countries, over the road across the hills, and every day, morning and evening, the border guard searched him, convinced that he would find whatever it was that Nasrudin was smuggling.

But the border guard found nothing.

Weeks went by. Months went by. Years went by. And still the two men played the same game each day. And still nothing.

At last the two men grew old and grey. The time came for the border guard to retire from his job. He searched Nasrudin for the last time. He found nothing.

That night, after he'd finished work, the border guard went round to Nasrudin's house.

'I just must know,' he said. 'You've been smuggling something all these years. Now you can put me out of my misery and tell me. I'm not a border guard any more. I retired today. Tell me. I can do nothing to you now. But I just must know.'

Nasrudin looked the border guard straight in the eye and smiled a little smile.

'Donkeys,' he said. 'Just donkeys.'

Every day Nasrudin had smuggled something as big as a donkey into the other country, right under the border guard's nose. The guard had been so busy searching for something that he thought was hidden much more carefully, he hadn't seen what was staring him in the face every day.

Often the answers we want are there in front of us. We only have to open our eyes to see them.

Prayer

Help us God, to see what is there to see. Help us to open our eyes and ears and to notice what is around us. Help us to be aware and help us to be awake. Help us to think clearly.

Amen

Hymn

'Hands to work and feet to run' *Someone's singing, Lord*

The factory and the hospital

There are two ways of tackling a problem. You can try to put right what you can see is wrong, or you can look back to the beginning and try to find out what caused the problem in the first place. I wonder which you think is the best way. Listen to today's story before you decide.

There was once a factory that had hundreds and hundreds of people working in it. The factory made machines that were then sent all over the world to other factories making more machines. This factory was very up-to-date and it had all the very latest electronic equipment in it. But unfortunately, it wasn't a very safe place to work in. Many people every day were hurt or injured. The complicated machinery on the production lines didn't take any account of people who might work a bit slowly, or who might make a mistake, or who might forget to do something, or who might in fact not know how to work the machine properly in the first place. Every day people came out of the factory with cuts or bruises or even squashed fingers. Sometimes the injuries were even more serious. Sometimes a worker died in the dreadful machinery of the factory.

At last people began to speak up.

'It isn't right that we should come to work and not be safe,' they said.

'Something ought to be done,' they said.

'People should not be getting injured like this,' they said.

Someone in the town volunteered to set up a first aid tent near the factory gates; like the sort of first aid tent you sometimes see at fêtes and garden parties.

'That's a good idea,' said the workers. And whenever anyone was hurt or injured, they went straight to the first aid tent, and the people there tried to help them.

Soon, more people became involved in the idea of the first aid tent, and the idea grew. The tent was replaced by a small clinic with a part-time doctor and nurse. The clinic was able to treat quite serious injuries as well as those that were not so serious.

After a while, the Town Council became involved, and gave some extra money to the clinic. The clinic was made bigger and it grew into a small hospital. There was enough money to give the hospital some very new equipment, and enough money to pay full-time doctors and nurses to work there. The hospital was kept very busy with all the people from the factory who needed looking after.

In the end, the people who were in charge of the factory saw how good and useful the hospital was, and they too gave a large amount of money to help to pay for it. They allowed the workers to go to the hospital at any time they needed to, and they even paid for an ambulance so that anyone who was seriously injured could be taken very quickly from the factory workshops to the hospital wards.

But, as each year went by and the factory got busier and busier making more and more machines, more and more workers were hurt and injured. The doctors and nurses at the hospital worked harder and harder, but in spite of everything they tried to do, more and more people died from the injuries they had received in the factory.

I wonder what *you* think should have happened? It was kind of the people to provide a first aid tent at the beginning of the story, but perhaps it would have been better if someone had looked at all the machinery that was hurting people and causing injuries, and tried to put that right. Then the hospital might not have been needed for the factory. Perhaps it could have been used to help other people instead.

Prayer
Dear God, when things go wrong, help us to look for the reason. Help us to try to put things right so that we don't make the same mistakes again. Help us not to do anything which could hurt other people. Help us to be safe.

Amen

Hymn
'I am planting my feet' *Come and Praise* Vol 2

Biblical references to the theme   *Week 8   Communication*

'How clearly the sky reveals God's glory!
How plainly it shows what he has done!
Each day announces it to the following day;
each night repeats it to the next.
No speech or words are used, no sound is heard;
yet their message goes out to all the world
and is heard to the ends of the earth.'

Psalms 19:1-4

'Pilate wrote a notice and had it put on the cross. "Jesus of Nazareth, the King of the Jews," is what he wrote.'

John 19:19

The notices

I wonder how many different kinds of notices you see on your way to school? You might see street signs and traffic signs. You might see signs and notices in shop windows. You might see a 'for sale' notice in a car window. There are lots of different notices, all saying different things.

We have notices in and around our school. Can you tell me what some of them are? Yes, and there's the welcome notice on the front door, the fire exit notices here in the hall, and the notice in the corridor that tells visitors where the school office is.

Notices give us information. Life would be very difficult if shops and schools and bus stations and towns didn't have notices to help people. But notices can say very different things. Listen to this story about some children who went on a school visit to a newspaper printers.

The whole class went together. The building was enormous. It was a busy, noisy, bustling, exciting place to visit. They started off, all together, in the main front office. The children were told that they would not be allowed to look round the newspaper building together; they would have to go in small groups.

The first group set off. They walked round the back of the office desks to the design department. This is where the newspaper layout was decided, and where the newspaper artists and draftsmen worked. Their office was big and bright and cheerful. There were colourful pictures and photographs and posters everywhere. There were notices on the walls and desks. The children read the notices.

'Welcome'
'Come in'
'Enter'
'Waiting area'
'Visitors this way'
'Secretary'

All the people working in the office were very friendly. They talked to the children and explained what they were doing. They gave them all a drink of coke or juice from a vending machine in the corner. They seemed happy that the children had come to see their office, and were pleased to show them all they could.

From there, the first group went through a big swing door. They were told that this next part of the building was dangerous to visitors because it housed machinery and the newspaper's printing presses. The children were told that they must keep in their group, they must keep to the special pathways, and they must do exactly as they were told. They set off down the corridor.

There were lots of doors leading off the corridor and each door had a notice on it. The children read them as they walked past.

'Private'
'No entry'
'Newspaper personnel only'
'Danger'
'Keep out'
'No admittance'
'Fire exit'

Eventually the children were taken through a door marked 'Machine room' and told to stand in one particular place. The noise was deafening. Eight huge printing presses were thundering out newspapers at the rate of hundreds every minute. Each printing press was threaded with a gigantic reel of paper. As the paper rushed through the machines it was printed, then cut and folded. Finished newspapers, ready for reading, were being stacked up by the machines. The printing presses were so noisy, and the machine room was such a dangerous place, that the children were only able to stay in there for a short time.

After the visit, all the children went back to school. Each group told the other groups what they had seen and where in the building they had been. All the children agreed that the friendliest part of the building had been the artists' office, and the unfriendliest part had been the machine room.

'Why do you say that?' their teacher asked.

'Because the notices in the artists' office were inviting us in, and the notices near the machine room were telling us to keep away,' said the children.

'And do you know why that was?' asked their teacher.

'Because the machine room was dangerous,' they said.

The children decided that they wanted to make their classroom into a newspaper building, and they spent the rest of the week planning it. They designed some model printing presses and planned an artists' office and a machine room. And of course, they made sure they had plenty of notices to warn people away, or to invite people in.

In a way, we are a bit like that newspaper building! We don't wear notices telling people that we're friendly or unfriendly, but we show people which we are by the way we talk and move. Let's make sure we try to give friendly signs to each other and that we don't wear invisible notices that say 'Keep away'.

Prayer

Dear God, please help us to be helpful and friendly towards each other.

Help us to remember that a smile is a friendly sign, and that one smile usually makes another one.

Amen

Hymn
'Think, think on these things'   *Someone's singing, Lord*

Practical ideas
With a little preparation, a variety of notices can be collected together and either arranged on a wall, or held up by children. We gathered our notices from around school, had the children hold them up at the front of the hall, then spent some time at the beginning of assembly rearranging them into groups. We collected together the notices that warn, those that inform, those that welcome, and those that direct. The children were able to say why each group of notices was necessary. As the story unfolded, the individual 'notices' mentioned in it came forward.

The hunter   *Week 8   Communication*
adapted from Islamic teaching

In our last assembly we talked about notices: notices that say in words or pictures exactly what they mean; notices that are easily understood. But sometimes it's possible to communicate, to show what you mean, without using words or pictures, signs or symbols at all. In today's story an animal showed a man what it wanted just by looking at him.

Nasrudin worked for the king. He was a good worker and always tried to do his best. In his spare time, he liked to go hunting, and the king allowed him to hunt in the royal forests.

One day Nasrudin was riding through the forest when he thought he saw something move in the long grass at the side of the track. He stopped his horse and listened and watched. Nothing. He stayed perfectly still. Nothing. He didn't move a muscle. Nothing . . . and then a tiny movement, a rustle of leaves, a tiny sound on the ground.

Silently Nasrudin climbed down from his horse and moved towards the long grass. There, lying curled up in a little hollow, and almost hidden by all the grass, was a tiny baby deer. A fawn. It was beautiful. It was the palest beige colour, with white spots on its back and sides. It had a tiny stumpy tail and big soft dark trusting eyes. It was all alone.

'You are lovely,' said Nasrudin quietly. 'My children would like to have you as a pet.' And without thinking any further, Nasrudin gently picked up the baby deer and lifted it up onto the horse's saddle. Nasrudin didn't think of the distress he might be causing the baby's mother, or of what he was going to do with the deer when he got home, or of how he shouldn't take animals from the wild. The only thing Nasrudin could think of was how beautiful the fawn was and how he wanted to share it with his children.

Nasrudin sat in the saddle carefully and held the fawn gently so as not to hurt it. He rode slowly so as not to frighten the fawn, but as he rode he had the strangest feeling something was following him. He turned to look, and there behind him was the baby deer's mother.

Usually deer are shy animals. They stay well hidden from people; they know that men sometimes hunt them. But Nasrudin knew why this deer was following him so openly. Nasrudin had only to look into her eyes to understand. For the look in her deep sad eyes pleaded with him to let her baby go. Nasrudin could see her thoughts mirrored in her eyes. Her thoughts said, 'Please let me have my baby back. I am out here on the track following your horse, and I know that you might kill me, but I don't care. I don't want to stay alive if I have to live without my baby.' Nasrudin looked into her eyes and knew what he must do.

He stopped his horse and gently slid out of the saddle and on to the ground. He carefully lifted the fawn down and walked with it to the edge of the track. He walked into the grass and laid the fawn down. Then he went back to his horse, mounted it and rode just a little way away. Then he watched to see what the mother deer would do.

She quickly ran to her baby. She licked it all over then nudged it to its feet with her soft nose. She walked with it back to the place where Nasrudin had first seen it. As she walked, the mother deer turned to look again at Nasrudin. Her eyes clearly showed that she was afraid of him, but that she was thankful that he had given her back her baby.

Nasrudin rode home and told his children about the deer. He also told them that they must always show kindness to all animals and never do anything to hurt them or cause them distress.

I'm glad that Nasrudin understood what the mother deer was trying to say. I'm glad that he was kind and let the baby go back to its mother.

Sometimes people, as well as animals, communicate what they need without using words, but with their eyes or their face or their body. We must make sure that we watch and listen, so that we know what people are trying to communicate.

Prayer

Dear God, help us to be sensitive to the needs of others. Help us to know that sometimes someone can ask for help without using words. Help us never to hurt animals or cause them any distress.

Amen

Hymn
'All the animals'   *Come and Praise* Vol 2

The story of book tokens   *Week 8   Communication*

What do you do if you want to find something out? Yes, usually you can look up whatever-it-is in a book. Just about anything you could want to know is in a book somewhere; it's a question of finding the right book.

Books are a very clever way of communicating. An author you've never met can write down his or her thoughts in a book, and you or anyone, anywhere in the world can read what he or she had to say. We have hundreds of books in our school, and I know you have lots of books at home. I like to be given books as presents, do you? Have you ever been given a book token, so that you can choose your own book? I think I like getting book tokens even better than being given a book, because then I can go to the bookshop myself and spend as long as I like choosing just the right book.

If you'd been a child 60 years ago, you couldn't have had a book token as a present, because they hadn't been invented. Here's how it all started.

Harold Raymond worked as a publisher; his factory made books. Harold liked books. He enjoyed reading in his spare time, and he loved to be given a book as a present. He had a large library at his house, where he kept all his books.

It was Christmas time in 1920. Harold's family were all together in his house. Some of his relatives had come from their homes, to spend Christmas at his. It was going to be a really good Christmas, he just knew it!

On Christmas morning everyone came downstairs, and there under the tree were the presents. An enormous pile of them. 'Good,' thought Harold, 'there's bound to be lots of books. I'll be able to read everyone else's as well as the ones I've been given. I just can't wait to open all those parcels.'

But Harold had to wait, because in their family the presents were not opened until after breakfast. Harold tried to hurry everyone up. At last it was time. They all sat round the tree and the presents were distributed. There were 119 presents to give out! Wrapping paper was torn off and gasps of 'Ooh' and 'Aah' were heard as people opened their presents. But Harold was very disappointed. Out of all the 119 presents, only three were books, and two of those were not for him.

After Christmas Harold talked to all his friends and asked them if they'd had many books given to them. But they hadn't, and Harold discovered it was because people didn't like to give books as presents if they weren't exactly sure what sort of books the person liked to read.

'Well, we'll have to do something about that, won't we,' said Harold, and he went home to think of a plan. Soon he had it. Book tokens. He went to a meeting of publishers and told them of his idea.

'People can give a book token as a present, then the person it's given to can go to any bookshop in the country, choose their own book and pay with the token instead of with money. It's a brilliant idea.'

'Oh no,' said his colleagues. 'It won't work. No-one will buy them. Forget it. It's not a good idea.'

But Harold persisted. He wasn't going to give up his idea. He was sure it would work. He went to a meeting of the National Book Council and told them about it.

'We don't think it will work,' they said. 'But we suppose we could try it.' The National Book Council didn't do anything about Harold's idea straight away. They waited six years before they sent out the first book tokens to the bookshops. The tokens were all alike, they had a picture of a bluebird on the front, and inside the card said 'The gift is mine, the choice is thine.' The Book Council expected the idea to fail.

That first year a few people bought book tokens. The next year, twice as many people bought tokens. The following year thousands of people bought tokens, and last year . . . well, last year £10 million worth of book tokens were sold. Twenty new cards are designed every Autumn, so there are now lots of different pictures to choose from. The words inside say 'For you to choose the book you want'.

Harold Raymond's idea had been a good one.

The next time you are given a book token as a present, you might remember Harold, who invented the idea of the very first one, because he was disappointed that he didn't have some books for Christmas.

Prayer

Thank you God, for books. Thank you for all the different kinds of books; story books, information books, puzzle books, books to make us laugh and books to make us think. Thank you for all the people who work to make books for us to read; the authors, the publishers, the printers, the book-sellers. Help us to remember to look after our books at home and at school.

Amen

Hymn
'Black and white'   *Come and Praise* Vol 1

Practical ideas
I found it helpful to show the children some examples of book tokens; some of our children had never had one. We made a display of some of our favourite books, together with the tokens. I included the book *Thank you for a book to read* by Patricia and Victor Smeltzer, published by Lion Books (ISBN 0 85648 242 0).

For further information about Book Tokens, write to Book Tokens Ltd, 152 Buckingham Palace Road, London SW1W 9TZ.

Biblical references to the theme   *Week 9   Summer*

'As long as the world exists, there will be a time for planting and a time for harvest. There will always be cold and heat, summer and winter, day and night.'

Genesis 8:22

'When you see their leaves beginning to appear, you know that summer is near.'

Luke 21:30

The school trip   *Week 9   Summer*

I wonder how many of you have been on a trip this summer? I know lots of you go to the seaside with your family at the weekends, and some of you have been on a trip to a theme park, or a visit to a zoo, or a picnic in the country. Everybody in our school has been on a visit with their class; most of you have been somewhere in connection with a topic you've been working on.

It's fun to go on an outing, isn't it? And it's fun to go in a group, and share the trip with your friends. It's really special to go on a school visit; to go out of school, somewhere different, all together with everyone else in your class. In today's story, a class of children went on a school visit, but things started to go wrong, and they thought the visit would be a disaster.

The day started well. All the children in class seven arrived at school early, and by ten to nine they were all sitting on the coach ready to go. They'd been planning the visit for weeks. They were going to Stump Cross Cavern, a huge complex of caves. They were going to be taken into the caves, deep underground. They knew the caves would be dark and damp and that they would see stalactites and stalagmites. They were all very excited about the visit.

At last, the boxes of sandwiches, bottles of squash, first aid things, papers, clipboards, pencils and all the other things they needed, were loaded on to the coach, and they all set off.

The coach drove out of the school gates, down the street, and out on to the main road. It followed the road for a couple of miles, went round the roundabout . . . and stopped!

'Why have we stopped here?' everyone asked.

'Are we there yet?'

'What are we doing?'

'What's happening?'

'I'm sorry,' said the driver. 'There seems to be something wrong with the engine. I think we've broken down.'

'Oh no,' everyone groaned. 'What are we going to do?'

'Stay where you are,' said the driver. 'I'll try to fix it.'

So the children stayed on the coach and the driver got out to try to fix the engine. After some considerable time, he climbed aboard again and said, 'Sorry. There's nothing I can do with it. I'm afraid I'll have to ring the garage and ask them to send out another coach, if they've got one spare. But it's going to take quite a while to get one here.'

Well, you can imagine how disappointed the children felt. 'Come on,' their teachers said. 'Let's get off the coach. There's a field over there, we'll ask if we can use it. It'll be better than sitting in the bus doing nothing.'

The children climbed down from the bus. They felt upset at the way things were turning out, but they were a cheerful class of children, and they always tried to make the best of things, so they were not miserable, or cross; no-one cried or had a tantrum.

One of the adults went to find the owner of the field. Two minutes later she was back, bringing with her a very small, very old, very unusual-looking woman. She was dressed from head to heel in dark green; dark green hat with a feather, green jacket, skirt, shirt, socks, and even shoes with green shoe-laces. She said she was the owner of the field. She said the children could use the field until their replacement coach came, as long as they didn't do any damage. The children said they wouldn't do any damage, but they didn't really think there was much damage they *could* do in a boring old field.

'Boring old field?' said Mrs Green. (That, believe it or not, was her name.) 'This field can teach you a thing or two. Come on.' And she led them into it.

Mrs Green took the children to an elderflower tree. She quickly snapped off a twig and showed them how to poke out the pith from the middle to make a thin tube. Then she pierced some holes into the pipe and blew down it. A lovely whistling sound came out. She left a group of children making pipes, and quickly whisked the rest of the class along to a privet hedge.

Here she pulled off a large leaf, folded it in half, and holding the leaf in both hands, blew gently. The leaf whistled. Mrs Green controlled the pointed end of the leaf and made the sound change. She played a tune on the leaf.

'You do it,' she said to six of the children. 'And you come with me,' she said to the rest, rushing them away to a bump in the grass. Suddenly she lay down on the earth with her ear to the ground. She listened. Then, just as suddenly, she jumped up, scrabbled in the soil and gently pulled out a small dark grey creature – a mole. The children were delighted. Mrs Green showed them the mole's big front paws, and tiny back ones. She showed them the mole's long snout and its eyes so small they could hardly be seen. The children touched the mole's soft velvety fur. Then, before they had time to think, they were hurried on to see the bank voles in the hedge-bottom, the family of field mice in the grass, the deserted blackbird's nest in the tree, and the baby hedgehogs under a bush. Mrs Green showed them how to make dancing ballerinas out of the fuchsia flowers hanging over the edge of the field from someone's garden.

Somehow, Mrs Green managed to sort out the groups of children so that everyone saw everything and had a turn at making all the things she had shown them how to do. And in the middle of all this activity, Mr Green appeared in the field with jugs of fresh orange juice, lemonade, and chocolate chip cookies. Then the replacement coach arrived.

The children once again felt disappointed; but this time because they had to stop what they were doing and leave the field and Mr and Mrs Green. However, their teachers made arrangements for the Greens to visit the children at school, and for the children to visit the Green's field again.

'Thank you. We'll never say a field is boring again,' shouted the children, as the new coach pulled away to take the class to the caves.

When the coach broke down, the children thought their visit was spoiled, but it turned out to be even better than they'd planned. I wonder if Mr and Mrs Green would have been so helpful to the class if they'd all been miserable and cross because of the coach breaking down? What do you think?

If something unusual has ever happened to you on a trip, you could write it down for me and I'll put all the writing in a book.

Prayer

Thank you God, for visits and trips and outings. Help us to make days out happy for the people who go with us, as well as for ourselves. Help us to be cheerful and to make the best of things, even when things go wrong.

Amen

Hymn

'The best gift' *Come and Praise* Vol 1

Practical ideas

The 'throw-away' remark at the end of this assembly, asking children to write down their unusual experiences on outings, brought forth a quantity of pieces of writing and art work. These were, as promised, assembled into books and displayed on the hall walls for all to see.

I find that such requests in assemblies, providing they are not made too often, do bring a good response from the children, and do provide a quick and simple way of having all ages in school contributing towards a single goal, without it cutting across classroom topics. Children often prepare this sort of work at home or in their spare time, and are prepared to put in effort when they know it is valued and to be put to specific use.

A woman and a dog   *Week 9   Summer*
adapted from Islamic teaching

Do you ever feel thirsty? I do, especially in the summer time when it's hot. There's no problem, of course, when we feel thirsty, because we go and get a drink. But animals can't help themselves to drinks, and if you have a pet at home, you have to make sure it has clean water to drink all the time. In today's story, a dog was thirsty but it couldn't find any water; neither could it find anyone to help it, until it met an old woman.

The weather was extremely dry. The dog was a stray and had no home in any particular place. He just wandered about, finding food and water where he could. But for three days he had had neither. No-one had given him any food, and he had been unable to find water for himself. He was dying of thirst.

There were no puddles or pools where he could drink. There were no rivers or streams. Everywhere was dry as dust. He lay down by the side of the road, and knew he would soon die.

An old woman came past. She was not a kind woman. She had led a bad life and was interested only in herself. She had no family and no friends.

No-one was kind or helpful to her, and she saw no reason to be kind or helpful to anyone else. She walked along the road towards the town.

She saw the dog lying by the side of the road. She saw the flies on its fur; she saw the glazed look in its eyes, and saw its tongue lolling out of its mouth. She knew that by the time she came back along this road, the dog would be dead. She knew there was nothing she could do to help it.

The old woman continued walking along the road towards the town, but for some reason, the picture of the dog who was dying, would not leave her mind.

'There was nothing I could do,' she said to herself, but even while she was saying it, she knew that the dog might live if it had a drink of water.

'But there is no water near here,' she said. 'I can't help it.'

As the old woman was thinking this, she saw a well across the other side of the field. She hurried towards it and leaned over the circular wall of the well. She looked down, down, deep into the well shaft. There, such a distance down, was water. But there was no bucket at the well. The handle had broken, and the winding gear that used to lower the bucket down into the water was gone.

'There's no way I can get any water for the dog,' she said to herself. 'The well is too deep, and there is no bucket. There is nothing I can do.' But the picture of the dog still would not leave her mind.

Suddenly she had an idea. She took off the scarf she was wearing on her head, and tore it into strips. She tied all the strips together to make a long length of cloth. Then, she took off one of her shoes and tied the end of the cloth round the shoe. Quickly, she lowered the shoe down into the well, down past the level of the water. Gently, she pulled the shoe up to the head of the well. Carefully, she carried the shoe, brimful of water, back along the road to the dog. He was still alive.

She poured a few drops of water into his mouth. He didn't move. She gave him a few more drops. He began to lick. She offered him the shoe. He turned his head and began to lap the water from it. After a while he sat up. Then he stood. Soon he licked her hand and trotted off down the road. The old woman emptied the last drops of water out of her shoe, and put it on again. She felt happy that she had been able to help the dog. She had never had such a feeling as this before, because she had never helped anyone before.

The old woman asked Allah to forgive her past bad ways, and she promised that she would try to live a good life in the future. Later, the Prophet Mohammed (peace be upon him), said

'I saw that old woman in Heaven.'

Prayer
Remind us Lord, to give help when we can. Teach us never to turn away from those who need help. Help us never to let animals suffer, when we can do something to help them.

Amen

Hymn
'From the tiny ant' *Come and Praise* Vol 2

A Midsummer Night's Dream
adapted from Shakespeare

Week 9 Summer

Midsummer's Day can be celebrated on the longest day of the year – June 21st – or on the official calendar day, which is the 24th June. There are many stories about magical things which can happen on Midsummer's Day, but perhaps the most famous of all is the story of *A Midsummer Night's Dream*. This was written 400 years ago, by a man called William Shakespeare.

Hermia was a beautiful girl. She had been commanded by her father to marry a man called Demetrius. Hermia said she couldn't marry Demetrius because she didn't love him. She loved Lysander. But her father insisted she marry Demetrius, and said she had four days to make up her mind to marry him, or else he would have her killed for not doing as she was told.

Hermia was very unhappy, and went to tell Lysander what her father had said.

'Don't worry,' said Lysander. 'We'll run away. Then he can't make you marry Demetrius. Meet me in the wood tonight, but don't tell anyone.' Hermia said she wouldn't, but then went to tell her friend Helena the secret.

That night, Hermia, then Lysander, crept quietly into the wood. Neither of them knew that Helena, and Demetrius, were already there, waiting to see what would happen. And neither Hermia, Lysander, Helena, nor Demetrius, knew that there were others in the wood as well as them.

Oberon and Titania, the king and queen of the fairies, were there, quarrelling. 'I know what I'll do,' said King Oberon to himself. 'I'll play such a trick on her.' And he called for his favourite magician.

'Puck,' he said. 'Go and get some magic flower potion. Wait until Queen Titania is asleep, and sprinkle some on her eyes. When she wakes up she'll fall in love with the first creature she sees. Then . . . Wait . . . What's that . . .?' Puck and King Oberon stood quite still and listened. They saw the four humans coming separately into the wood. Immediately, King Oberon knew about Hermia's problem with Demetrius and Lysander.

'Puck,' he said. 'Sprinkle some of that magic potion on the eyes of Demetrius. But be sure to do it when Helena is near. Then he will fall in love with her, and all will be well.

Puck did as he had been asked. First he sprinkled the magic drops on the eyes of Queen Titania, then he went to find Demetrius. But by mistake, he put the magic drops on *Lysander*'s eyes. Lysander woke, saw Helena, and fell in love with her. Puck realised what a dreadful mistake he had made, and went to find Demetrius. Quickly he sprinkled the magic potion on Demetrius's eyes. Demetrius woke, also saw Helena, and fell in love with her!

'Oh no,' said Puck. 'What am I going to do? They both love Helena.' But before he had time to do anything, Hermia came and saw that both Lysander and Demetrius were in love with Helena: Helena who was her best friend. In minutes the four of them were arguing, and Lysander and Demetrius were beginning to fight.

'Quick,' said King Oberon to Puck. 'Put a thick mist around the wood, so that none of them can see. You must stop the fight. You must find a way to put another potion on Lysander's eyes so that he will fall in love with Hermia again, and all will return to normal.'

Meanwhile, a group of tradesmen had come into the wood to practise a play they were going to perform for the Duke. Bottom, the weaver, put on a donkey head mask. He frightened the others so much that they all ran away! Bottom was left alone, and to prevent himself from feeling afraid, he started to sing.

The song woke up Queen Titania. Because of the magic potion, she fell in love with Bottom-the-weaver-in-the-donkey-head-mask, as soon as she saw him. She hugged him to her, stroked his furry face, and let him go to sleep in her arms.

When King Oberon saw that his trick had worked, he decided it was time to put everything right again. He asked Puck to mix a new magic potion that would cancel the effect of the first one, and he sprinkled it on the eyes of those who needed it.

Lysander and Hermia were reunited. Demetrius and Helena were together again. Queen Titania saw Bottom the weaver for what he was, and fell in love once again with King Oberon. Just when it was almost happy ever after, Hermia's father came into the wood.

'Well? Have you decided that you will marry Demetrius?' he roared. All eyes turned to him. And magically, he understood. He gave permission for Hermia to marry Lysander. All the weddings were celebrated in style, and Bottom the weaver and the other tradesmen performed their play for everyone.

You can make of this story what you want, but if you find it in any way odd or unusual, you must remember that it's just a midsummer night's dream!

Prayer

Thank you God, for summer. Thank you for the magic of midsummer. Thank you for the stories and legend, fact and fiction, of midsummer. Help us, whenever we can, to make things end happily, like the story of a midsummer night's dream.

Amen

Hymn

'Round, round, round' *Come and Praise* Vol 2

Biblical references to the theme

Week 10   Sports

'So I run straight towards the goal in order to win the prize,'

Philippians 3:14

'Run your best in the race of faith, and win eternal life for yourself;'

1 Timothy 6:12

'I have done my best in the race, I have run the full distance, and I have kept the faith.'

2 Timothy 4:7

Christopher wins a gold

Week 10   Sports

Everyone is good at something. Everyone in our school knows that. Some people are good at painting or drawing, others are good at maths or technology, others are good at reading, or telling stories, or jumping, or helping, or listening, or science, or music. Everyone's good at something. But sometimes in life, being good isn't quite enough. And sometimes in life, surprising things happen.

Christopher was a lovely baby. He had dark hair, and blue eyes that watched his mother whatever she was doing. But although Christopher watched carefully, his mother soon noticed that he didn't listen carefully. She took him to the doctor, who said 'I'm sorry, but the reason Christopher doesn't listen carefully, is because he can't hear. He's deaf.'

When Christopher was old enough to go to school, he went to a special school for deaf children, and he worked very hard. He learned to do many of the things that you do at school. He learned to read and write; he did maths and science, PE and art, but his favourite lesson was games. He liked running and jumping, and ball skills.

Christopher worked hard every year at school, and when he was old enough he went to university. Sometimes, the work at university was difficult for him, because he couldn't hear what the teachers were saying. He watched their lips, and tried to work out what the words were. But sometimes they talked too quickly for him, and sometimes they turned their head away and he couldn't see their face. But he kept on trying, and he continued to work hard even though it was difficult. After four years, Christopher was awarded his degree, and it was time for him to find a job.

He went to firms and factories, shops and offices, but everyone said 'Sorry Christopher, we can't give you a job, because you can't hear.' Christopher felt it was very unfair that he wasn't given a job just because he couldn't hear. He could do everything else well, even better than some hearing people.

But at last, someone did offer him a job. 'You can come and work for us and be a gardener,' said the Council. This wasn't really the sort of job that Christopher wanted, but he decided that any job was better than no job, so off he went to be a gardener.

In his spare time Christopher went running. He decided to run in a marathon. He trained hard. He joined an athletics team and he worked hard in that. He tried his hand at an athletic event called throwing the hammer. He trained most evenings. Soon he was entering competitions and winning. His team were proud of him.

One day, his athletics coach said to him, 'Christopher, we'd like you to represent England at the Olympic Games for the Deaf, next summer. Will you come with us to New Zealand?' Christopher said he would very much like to do that.

Christopher trained really hard now. He knew he would be competing against other deaf athletes from all over the world. He knew that he was determined to do his best.

The time came to set off for New Zealand. Christopher set off with the rest of the team to catch the plane that would take them to the other side of the world for the Olympic Games for the Deaf.

The Games started. Athletes and gymnasts began to win medals. A silver for France, a gold for America, a bronze for Canada. Christopher's turn came. He had three hammer throws to do. The first was not his best. Try harder. The second was better. Good. But the third was his best ever, and the best in the competition. Christopher had won a gold.

Christopher tried hard in everything he did. He didn't get the job he wanted, but he found success in a different way, by doing his best and by trying hard. I think he deserved to win a gold medal, don't you?

Prayer

Dear God, help us to do our best in everything we do. Help us not to give up if something doesn't go the way we expect it to. Help us to know that sometimes success can come in surprising ways.

Amen

Hymn

'Hands to work and feet to run' *Someone's singing, Lord*

Sports Day

Week 10   Sports

There are different kinds of sports competitions. Sometimes you compete against other people in a race, where the winner is the one who comes first. Sometimes you compete against yourself, and you win if you beat your own record. Listen carefully to today's story, and see if you can decide which kind of competition it was in this school Sports Day.

Everyone in the whole school was looking forward to Sports Day. The children in Mr Howard's class had been practising events for weeks. He'd spent a long time explaining about the different races they were going to take part in, and how the day was to be organised. But two children didn't listen. They were too busy watching each other to take much notice of what Mr Howard was saying.

The two children, Leroy and Channah, were great rivals. They were always trying to beat each other, and everyone else, at everything. Each of them always wanted to be the best, or the first, or the winner.

The day before Sports Day, Mr Howard took the class out on to the playing field to time them in the 100 metre sprint. He used a stopwatch and wrote down on his clipboard how long each child took. Everyone did their best. Leroy and Channah were the fastest and both took exactly the same time to run the 100 metres.

Channah felt very cross with herself. She had expected that her time would be faster than Leroy's. She wondered how she would manage to beat him and win the race tomorrow. She was determined she *was* going to beat him and win.

Channah decided that if she couldn't beat Leroy by running faster, she would have to beat him by cheating. But how could she cheat in a running race? Suddenly she knew. She remembered the toy car that she had brought to school a few days ago; the toy car that Leroy had very much wanted. She would bring it to school tomorrow, and she would use it to help her win the race and to make Leroy lose.

Sports Day arrived. It was as warm and sunny as everyone had hoped it would be. The mums and dads all came to watch. The field was marked out for all the different events. Mr Howard's class was ready to start their races, and the 100 metre sprint was to be the first.

The children stood on the starting line. Channah made sure she stood next to Leroy. In the pocket of her shorts was the toy car . . . all ready . . . waiting.

Ready, steady, GO!

They were off, all speeding as fast as they could down the track. Channah and Leroy were level.

'Now,' she thought, and she pulled the toy car out of her pocket. She threw it down on the grass just in front of Leroy's feet, and kept on running as though she knew nothing about it.

Leroy saw the toy car, and just as Channah hoped he would, he thought that she had accidentally dropped it. He stopped running and bent to pick it up. 'I'll keep it,' he thought. He put it in his pocket and started running again, but by now of course, Channah was well in front and was crossing the finishing line.

'I've done it,' she thought. 'I've beaten him and everyone else. I've won.'

She stood proudly at the finishing line, waiting for Mr Howard to award her with the blue first-prize rosette, but to her amazement he walked straight past her, and pinned the rosette on a boy called Calum, instead.

'Why's he won?' said Channah. 'It's me. I'm the winner. I want the rosette.'

'No,' said Mr Howard. 'You can't have been listening. The winner is the one who beats their own record. Why do you think we did all that practising? Why do you think I timed you all? Calum didn't come first in this race, but that doesn't matter. He's beaten his record. He's run faster than he's ever run before. The prize is his.'

Channah looked embarrassed. 'I'm sorry,' she said. 'I didn't know.'

'No,' said Mr Howard. 'You didn't know because you didn't listen. Perhaps you could listen more carefully next time. Oh, and by the way, this is yours I think.' And he took the toy car from Leroy and gave it back to Channah.

I think Mr Howard knew that Channah had tried to cheat her way to winning the race. It was a pity she hadn't listened to Mr Howard earlier, she might have understood what kind of competition she was really in.

Can you tell me about that school's Sports Day? Were they running races where the winner was the one who came first, or were they beating their *own* records?

Prayer
Help us God, to do our best in everything we do.
Help us to try to better our best, so that we achieve more than we think we can.
Help us to gain our rewards through hard work and honesty, and not through cheating.
Help us never to spoil other people's efforts, but to value them.

Amen

Hymn
'Praise the Lord in everything'   *Come and Praise* Vol 1

A star is Bjorn   *Week 10   Sports*

Have you ever wondered how a sports champion comes to be a champion? Perhaps you think it's just luck. Or perhaps you think that the person was always good at that particular sport from when they were a tiny child. Or perhaps you think it's because they work very hard at their sport, and practise a lot. Maybe you think it's a mixture of all these things. Today I'm going to tell you the story of how someone came to be a Wimbledon tennis champion.

He was born in Sweden in 1956, and his parents named him Bjorn. The family liked sports of all kinds, and almost as soon as Bjorn could walk, he was encouraged to join in whatever the family was doing. He tried lots of different sports; the family's favourite was table tennis, but Bjorn soon discovered that his favourite was ice hockey. He was a good player, and by the time he was nine years old, he had been chosen to play for his town's junior team.

'I'm going to play for Sweden when I grow up,' he told his mother and father. 'I'm going to be an ice hockey champion.'

'We'll see,' said his parents.

One day soon after Bjorn's ninth birthday, his father took part in a table tennis tournament, and came first. The prize was a tennis racquet.

'You can have it,' he said to Bjorn, and he gave him the racquet. Bjorn went straight outside into the garden and began to hit a ball against the garage wall. It was fun. He could alter the speed at which he sent the ball, and he could spin it so that it came back at a different angle.

'I'd like to join the tennis club,' he said to his parents later.

'Then we'll go along tomorrow and see if there's a place for you,' said his mum. They went the next day to try to enrol Bjorn in the beginners' class, but it was full.

'We have a long waiting list,' said the club manager. 'I can put your name down, but you won't be able to start for quite some time.'

Bjorn was disappointed, and his mum thought he would probably give up the idea of wanting to join the club, by the time he was offered a place, but Bjorn didn't give up. Instead, he practised playing tennis, by himself, using the garage wall as a partner, every day for the next few months, until the tennis club gave him a place, and he could start having proper lessons.

Soon it became clear that Bjorn was an excellent tennis player.

'You should give up your other sports,' said his teacher, 'and concentrate on tennis.' Bjorn said no. He wanted to play lots of different sports and wait until he was older to choose just one. But things didn't work out quite like that. Bjorn began to win competitions. He began to compete in championships. He began to represent his country in competitions abroad. And he began to win.

Bjorn had to give up the other sports he enjoyed, in order to work even harder at tennis. When he was 15, he even gave up school, so that he could spend all his time practising.

People who watched Bjorn play noticed that not only was he very good at tennis, he was also a very good sportsman. He was always fair to his opponents, he never tried to cheat. He always did his best and tried his hardest. He never lost his temper, even when he made a mistake. He never shouted or sulked if he lost. He never behaved badly.

By now, Bjorn had been chosen to play tennis in most of the major tournaments in the world. He played in France and Sweden, America and Italy. At last he came to play tennis in England, at the Wimbledon Championships. 'A star is Bjorn', said the headlines in all the newspapers.

Bjorn played his best, and won the Championship. The next year he won again. The following year, he won again. And again. And again. He won the title five times in succession. He was the greatest player in the world.

The next year, 1981, Bjorn came to Wimbledon again, but this time he lost to John McEnroe. But he lost with good grace. He didn't shout, or stamp, or get angry, or blame anyone else. He was proving he was still a good sportsman.

Then, Bjorn decided to give up competitive tennis. 'I'll still play tennis,' he said. 'But I'll play for fun. I'll not play in competitions any more. There are other things I want to do.'

Bjorn Borg had been the world's top tennis player for ten years. Some people say he is the greatest tennis player there has ever been.

When Bjorn Borg was playing tennis, huge crowds came to watch him. Some people queued all night and all day, to be sure to get a ticket. The crowds liked him because he was a good tennis player; but they also liked him because he played fair, worked hard, and always tried to do his best. He was a good sportsman.

We can't all be world champions, but we can all play fair, work hard, do our best, and be good sportsmen and women; just like Bjorn Borg.

Prayer
Thank you God, for our health and strength. Thank you for the sporting opportunities we have. Help us to play fair, to work hard, to do our best, and to be good sportsmen and women. Help us to be brave enough to give three cheers to those who have beaten us. Help us to be good losers as well as good winners.

Amen

Hymn
'For all the strength we have' *Someone's singing, Lord*

Biblical references to the theme

Week 11 Holidays

'Then the king gave a great banquet in Esther's honour and invited all his officials and administrators. He proclaimed a holiday for the whole empire and distributed gifts worthy of a king.'

Esther 2:18

'He blessed the seventh day and set it apart as a special day, because by that day he had completed his creation and stopped working.'

Genesis 2:3

A calm blue sea

Week 11 Holidays

Have you noticed how people like to go to very different places for their holidays? Some people like to go to the countryside and others like to go to the sea. Some people like to go abroad and some like to stay in Britain. People often choose to go on holiday to places that are different from where they live; to places they don't know. But, of course, places that are new to holiday-makers are well known to the people who live there all the time. The local people sometimes give advice to the holiday people; and it would be sensible of the holiday-makers to listen!

The Smith family were on holiday at the seaside in Yorkshire.

'Let's go and see those boats,' said Jane. So they walked down the hill to the Coble Landing. Here there were boats that had just come in from fishing in the bay, and boats that were waiting to go to sea. There were fishermen sorting out their nets and lobster pots, and other fishermen tinkering with the engines of the tractors that were used to pull the boats across the sands to the sea. It was a busy, bustling, interesting place.

Mrs Smith leaned against the railings on the top of the sea wall. She pointed across the long finger of rock jutting out into the sea.

'Let's walk out there and go swimming from those rocks,' she said.

A fisherman, who was hanging his nets over the railings, said, 'No, don't go swimming out there. The sea's too strong at the end of the Brig. If you want to go swimming, stay in the bay.'

Mrs Smith looked out at the blue sea. It looked so calm. The wind was rippling the surface slightly, and each tiny crest sparkled silver in the sunlight.

'It looks safe enough,' she said.

'Aye, it might look safe,' the fisherman said, 'But there's more than one drowned out there. Do you see those steps cut in the cliff?' He pointed to some stone steps leading up the cliff face from the rocky Brig.

'Yes,' said Mrs Smith.

'They were put there after a lady drowned. She was walking near the end of the Brig and got cut off by the tide. She couldn't climb the cliff and was swept out to sea.'

'She should have learned to swim,' said Mrs Smith unkindly, and she walked away from the fisherman and his nets, towards the Brig.

'Come on,' she said to her family.

They followed her down the Coble Landing and across the beach. They walked past the yacht club and onto the Brig itself. They clambered over the rocks and poked about in the pools. They found shells and crabs, strange darting fish and swirling seaweed. They walked further and further, out to sea, along the narrowing rock.

The sea was on three sides of them now. They walked out as far as they could go. It was hot and sunny and the sea looked friendly and inviting.

'I think I'll go in for a swim,' said Mrs Smith.

'But Mum, the man said we shouldn't,' said John.

'He's making a fuss about nothing,' said Mrs Smith. 'It looks perfectly safe. Anyone coming?'

'I don't think we should,' said Mr Smith. 'You never can tell with the sea.'

'Oh well, you would agree with the fisherman, wouldn't you!' shouted Mrs Smith. And she dumped her bag down on the rock, got out her swimming things, and started to get changed.

'Dad?' said John. 'Look out there. The sea's got bumps on it.' He pointed out to the open sea, on the side of the Brig away from the town. Sure enough, the sea that had looked so flat and calm, now had the ridges of a rising swell on it.

'Come on,' said Mr Smith. 'I think we'd better go. Pick up your mum's bag, John.'

No sooner had Mr Smith said that, than a ridge of water surged forward and sucked at their feet and legs. It pushed Jane over and bumped her against a rock. It swept the bag away from John, who was just reaching out for it. The bag disappeared under the surface of the water and suddenly reappeared several metres away.

Mrs Smith, her face white, stared at it then rushed towards Jane to grab hold of her.

Mr Smith tried to hurry his frightened family back along the rocks towards the land, but the rocky way they had walked on a few minutes ago, was now under water. The family was marooned.

The sky suddenly darkened. The sun hid behind clouds and a wind blowing off the sea felt chilly. Mr Smith shivered.

John started to cry. 'Dad? What are we going to do?'

Mr Smith didn't answer John, but suddenly waved his arms in the air, pointed and shouted.

There was a small boat chugging towards them.

'Jump when I say,' said the fisherman they'd seen earlier.

'Now! Again! Jump! Now!'

When they were all safely aboard his boat, he pushed an old grey blanket towards them.

'You'll never learn, will you! You're all alike, you visitors. Always think you know best. Good thing this time it was only the swimming bag got swept under. It could have been *you*.' And the fisherman rowed the Smith family back to safety.

The Smith family were lucky to be alive, and they certainly had a fright. They need not have done if they'd remembered that the sea is powerful and needs to be treated with respect, and if they'd listened to the advice of the local fisherman.

Prayer
Dear God, please help us to treat our world with respect. Help us to know that calm-looking places can have hidden dangers. Help us to know that we can cause difficulties if we are not careful and sensible.

Amen

Hymn
'I listen and I listen'   *Come and Praise* Vol 1

Mountain rescue   *Week 11   Holidays*

Yesterday we heard a story about a family who forgot how powerful the sea can be. Luckily they were only frightened and not hurt. In today's story, some young people thought there was no danger in a mountain, but the story doesn't end as happily as yesterday's.

They had gone to stay at the Youth Hostel; four teenagers on holiday, Rod and Michael, Tammy and Katie.
'We'll go to the mountains,' they said. So they went to the Youth Hostel in Patterdale in the Lake District.
One day they decided to climb up to the top of a mountain they could see from the windows.
'It's called Helvelyn,' said the warden. 'But it needs treating with respect. Don't try to go up it today, the weather'll worsen later. Wait for another day or two.'
But the four friends didn't want to wait a day or two. They wanted to go up the mountain on *that* day.
'It'll be all right,' said Rod.
'Look, there's a notice here, telling you what to wear, and to take a rucksack with food and drink with you,' said Tammy, pointing to a notice board near the doorway of the Youth Hostel.
'Emergency rations – chocolate and fruit,' read Katie.
'Map, compass and sweater,' read Michael.
'You have to wear walking boots and an anorak,' said Tammy.
'I'm not,' said Rod. 'Trainers are O.K. And it's too hot for an anorak. I'm going as I am in this T shirt and shorts. Come on.'
They all trooped out of the door after Rod. They followed the path to the base of the mountain. Soon the path became a rocky track and they had to walk one behind the other like follow-my-leader. Rod was out in front.
'Hey, look at that,' said Tammy, and she pointed to the top of the mountain. A dark grey mist was beginning to roll down towards them.

'And look at that!' called Michael.

They all stopped to look at the track ahead. It was climbing quite steeply now and was even narrower than before. Just ahead of them the track changed to a narrow ridge with a steep drop at either side. Each sloping side was covered with small slippery stones. If they wanted to follow the track up to the top of the mountain, they would have to cross the dangerous ridge.

'Let's go back,' said Michael.

'No. Let's go across it,' said Katie.

'But that mist is coming down the mountain,' said Tammy. 'You know what the warden said about the weather.'

'I'm not going back. I'm going on,' said Rod. 'Anyone coming?'

'Yes, me,' said Katie.

Michael and Tammy turned and started to go back down the mountain.

Rod and Katie began to walk along the ridge. It was frightening once they were on it. The steep sloping sides made them feel dizzy. And, as they walked, the rolling mist began to swirl around them. It was thick and wet. Soon they were both soaked to the skin and their teeth were chattering. Worse, they could no longer see where they were going.

'Rod, I'm scared,' said Katie.

'Maybe we'd better wait until this mist goes,' said Rod, and he turned round to face Katie. But, as he manoeuvred on the narrow ridge, he slipped, and with a scream he slithered down the mountainside. Then there was silence.

'Rod?' called Katie.

'I'm down here,' said Rod. 'I think I've broken my ankle,' and he started to cry.

Michael and Tammy had been back at the hostel for ages, and still the other two hadn't turned up. It began to grow dark.

'Let's tell the warden they're missing,' said Michael.

Tammy went to explain about Rod and Katie crossing the ridge. She told him they had no warm clothing and no emergency food. She said they were wearing trainers and not walking boots.

The warden looked angrily at Tammy and went to 'phone the police. The police telephoned the mountain rescue team, and they were quickly at the Youth Hostel with their dogs and landrovers. They asked Michael and Tammy some questions, then set off into the night with their torches and lanterns.

At two in the morning, they found Rod and Katie huddled together on the scree. She had climbed down the slippery stones to be with Rod, but he couldn't climb up. The rescue team called out a helicopter, and an hour later they were hauled to safety and Rod was taken to hospital.

Later, back at the hostel, the police and the mountain rescue team had a great deal to say to Michael, Katie and Tammy!

Perhaps you can guess what the police said to the teenagers?

It was lucky that no-one was killed. The four were very silly because not only did they put themselves in danger, they endangered the lives of the rescue team who had to go out and search for them. Perhaps Rod learned the hard way that holiday places can be dangerous, and that warning signs and notices are there to help people to be safe.

Prayer
Dear God, please help us to be safe on holiday. Help us to remember that everything we do can affect other people as well. Help us to do nothing to endanger our own lives or the lives of other people. Help us to be safe.
Amen

Hymn
'Go, tell it on the mountain' *Come and Praise* Vol 1

Prince Radleigh's second holiday   *Week 11   Holidays*

There are lots of different kinds of holidays. There are seaside holidays, country holidays, activity holidays and lazy holidays. There are holidays in caravans, boats, hotels, tents, and other people's houses. There are holidays abroad and holidays at home. But the one thing that all holidays have in common, is that they are a change. They are different from usual. They are not the same as school and work.

Holidays should be fun for everyone. You might have heard the story of Prince Radleigh, who went on holiday to the seaside and had a wonderful time, but no-one else enjoyed it because they spent the whole time rushing about doing just what *he* wanted to do. At the end of the holiday everyone heaved a huge sigh of relief and said 'never-ever-ever-again.'

But Prince Radleigh did go on holiday again.

As the summer days grew longer, Prince Radleigh started to pester, 'Can we have another holiday, please? Oh please.'

'We all said never-ever-ever-again, after last time,' said the Queen. 'You wore everyone out.'

'But this year it'll be different,' said the Prince, 'I won't be selfish, I promise.' 'We *will* go on holiday,' said the King. 'But you're right. This year it *will* be different. This year we're going in a caravan.'

'Oh goody!' shouted Prince Radleigh, who was already imagining his own private caravan, filled with all his toys and games and books and animals. 'That'll be fun. How many caravans are coming?'

'One!' said the King. 'Just one. We're taking no servants. We're going to do everything ourselves; washing up, cooking, making the beds, and you're going to help.'

Prince Radleigh looked horrified.

'Furthermore,' said the King, 'You can take only one book, one game, one toy, one animal, and one bag of clothes.'

Prince Radleigh looked aghast.

'And,' went on the King, 'We're going to a place that *I* have chosen. I am not going to say where it is until we get there. Now, you can go and pack your things.'

Prince Radleigh burst into tears, but he went to his playroom to choose what to take. 'This is going to be the horriblest holiday!' he said.

The next day the King hitched a small caravan to the back of the royal golden coach. Then he and the Queen put in it all the things they would need for the week's holiday. Prince Radleigh put in his one book, one game, one toy, one animal, and one bag of clothes.

They set off.

The King drove and drove and drove for miles. Prince Radleigh had no idea where they were.

Suddenly, the King stopped the caravan. 'We're here,' he said, and he pointed to a field. They opened the field gate and drove in. They parked the caravan and unpacked.

Prince Radleigh looked with dismay at the field. 'But what are we going to do all week?' he asked.

'We're going to have fun,' said the King.

Prince Radleigh couldn't imagine how on earth they were going to have fun in the middle of a field, with none of the luxuries of the palace around them.

He decided this holiday would be dreadful.

His mum asked him to help get the tea ready. He had no idea what to do; he'd never helped before. Later, he had to help with the washing up, in a plastic bowl, outside.

Then his dad decided he wanted to play cricket, and please would the Queen and Prince Radleigh come and join in because he couldn't play cricket on his own. And for the first time ever, Prince Radleigh found himself doing what other people wanted him to do, instead of what *he* wanted to do. He went to bed that night feeling very cross.

The next morning was sunny and warm. He thought he'd go and explore, but his mum wanted him to help with the breakfast, then his dad wanted him to collect some wood so they could have a camp-fire that evening. By then it was lunch time, and Prince Radleigh had to help again.

After lunch the King asked him to help rig up a washing line so that he could wash his socks and hang them out to dry.

All day it was the same. Prince Radleigh was busy doing what the others wanted him to do. But, he suddenly discovered that he liked helping; he liked doing jobs. As the week went on, he became busier and busier. He helped with all the caravan jobs, he went for walks with his mum and dad, he played games with them. He found that he didn't miss all his books and games and toys at all.

But the biggest surprise of all came at the end of the week when they were going home. The caravan was packed ready for the long journey back to the palace. They set off, out of the field, up a lane, down a road, round a corner . . . and they were home! Back at the palace! Going up the royal drive!

'How did you do that?' asked Prince Radleigh.

'Easy,' laughed the King. 'We were only in a field at the end of the palace grounds. I drove a long way round to make you think we'd travelled a long way. You see, you don't have to go a long way from home to have a good holiday!'

'And I *have* had a good holiday,' said Prince Radleigh. 'Can we go again?'

'We'll see,' said the King. 'We'll see.'

At least this time the King didn't say 'never-ever-ever-again'. I'm glad the Prince enjoyed his holiday in the end. And I'm glad that the King and Queen liked it too.

It was interesting that Prince Radleigh started to enjoy the holiday when he started to help other people, wasn't it?

Prayer
Thank you God, for holidays. Help us to remember that holidays belong to everyone. Help us to make our holidays enjoyable for everyone who's with us.

Amen

Hymn
'The flowers that grow in the garden'   *Someone's singing, Lord*

Biblical references to the theme

Week 12   Endings

'The end of anything is better than its beginning. Patience is better than pride.'

Ecclesiastes 7:8

'God looked at everything he had made, and he was very pleased. Evening passed and morning came – that was the sixth day.'

Genesis 1:31

'I am the first and the last, the beginning and the end.'

Revelation 22:13

Saint Swithin

Week 12   Endings

Have you heard the saying about St Swithin's Day? It says that if it rains on St Swithin's Day it will rain for the next 40 days. There's a rhyme you might know;

St Swithin's Day, if you do rain,
For forty days it will remain.
St Swithin's Day, if you be fine,
For forty days the sun will shine.

St Swithin's Day is always on July 15th, always near the end of our school year. Most people have heard of him and the saying about the rain, but not many people know the story behind it.

Saint Swithin was Bishop of Winchester over a thousand years ago. He was a good man and spent his life trying to help poor people. It was his wish that when he died, he should be buried outside the church, with the ordinary people. You see, in those days, important people were buried inside the church and were given elaborate memorial stones with their names written on. Ordinary people were buried outside the church, in unmarked graves.

'When I die, I want to be buried outside the church,' he said. 'Near the path where people walk.'

Later, when Bishop Swithin died, the people remembered what he had said, and because they respected his wishes, they buried him outside the church.

But the new Bishop of Winchester said, 'It is not right that the body of such an important man should be laid to rest outside the church, surrounded by the graves of the poor. He should have a place of honour, here, inside the church.'

'But he wanted to be outside,' said his friends.

'No. It is not right,' said the Bishop. 'He must be moved, and given this place of honour.'

So arrangements were made for Bishop Swithin's body to be moved inside the church.

But, on the day on which the move was to take place, it rained.

'We'll wait until tomorrow,' said the workmen.

The next day it rained even harder. Heavy rain. Storm-force rain. Rain which stopped all work of every kind.

'Tomorrow,' said the men.

But there was rain and then more rain.

'Tomorrow or tomorrow,' said the men.

And still the rain continued.

Someone was keeping count of the rain days.

36, 37, 38, 39 days.

'Will it never stop?' the people asked.

'It will stop when we stop the plans to move Bishop Swithin,' said someone.

'You're right,' said someone else. 'All this rain is because we want to move him. We're no longer doing what he wanted. He wanted to rest in peace outside the church.'

'Perhaps you're right,' said the new Bishop. 'Maybe we should stop our plans.'

'Yes,' said the people.

'Then it shall be so,' said the new Bishop. 'He shall rest in peace where he is.'

The workmen hurried home, dodging the drops as they went.

The next day, the fortieth day, the rain stopped and the sun shone out, watery at first, then stronger, brighter.

And so started the legend of St Swithin's Day; that if it rains on this day, it'll rain for 40 more.

I hope it doesn't rain *this* St Swithin's Day, or we might have a very wet end of term and summer holiday.

Prayer
Dear God, thank you for all the stories and legends of the saints. Thank you for all the people who, throughout history, have tried to lead good lives and help other people. Help us to help others when we can.

Amen

Hymn
'Water of life'   *Come and Praise* Vol 1

Hard work!
adapted from Aesop

Have you worked hard this year? Now that we're at the end of term and can look back over the whole year, what can you see? Can you see yourself doing your best and working hard all year? I *know* we have hard-working children, and teachers, at our school. And it's hard work, working hard, isn't it! But it's worth it when you achieve something; when you learn something new or finish something you've been making.

In today's story, a farmer knew the value of hard work and wanted to teach his sons about it, but he knew they were lazy boys, so he had to trick them.

The old farmer knew he hadn't much longer to live. Soon his sons would be in charge of the farm. They would have to dig the earth, look after the vines and gather in the grapes for the wine. But the farmer knew that his sons were lazy boys. He feared that after he was gone, they would laze away their days and let the farm go to waste.

It would be such a pity if that happened. The farm was just beginning to prosper after all his years of hard work. Somehow he had to make his sons understand that the only way to become rich, was through hard work. But how could he make them understand? They only worked hard when he was there, telling them what to do; and soon he would be gone.

Then the farmer had an idea. He called his sons to him.

'Boys,' he said. 'I know I'm going to die soon. I want you to know that you'll find all my treasure hidden in the vineyard.'

The sons wanted him to tell them exactly where the treasure was buried, but the farmer would say no more.

Soon, the old man died.

For six days his sons did no work. Then the youngest boy said, 'Let's go look for the treasure in the vineyard.'

So they took spades and hoes, forks and rakes, and dug in the vineyard to search for the treasure. They imagined they would find a box, a chest, filled with gold pieces. Or maybe a sack stuffed with silver. Or even a bag of bronze. They turned the soil over and over and dug deep into the rich dark earth. When they reached the end of the vineyard and found nothing, they went back to the beginning and started all over again, convinced that the buried treasure was there somewhere, and determined to find it.

By the end of the day they found nothing, not a single silver piece; but the soil had been well turned and there wasn't a weed in sight.

The next day, the sons started again early. They dug and turned the soil; they hoed, raked, forked and delved. As they went, they trimmed and tidied the rows of vines – no use having them straggling, might as well tidy them up as they go along.

At the end of the day – nothing.

At the end of the week – nothing.

At the end of the month – nothing. But by now they had the best cared for vineyard in the country. By now the vines were thriving. By now the boys were used to the routine of getting up early and working in the vineyard all day.

And still they kept searching. The vines grew well. And still they kept digging. The grapes grew better than ever before. And still they kept turning the soil, over and over, searching for treasure.

The grapes were harvested; more than usual. The wine was made; the best in the land. Everyone wanted to buy it.

The brothers became rich and they prospered. They earned a fortune, just as their father had intended, through hard work.

The brothers still searched for the treasure, every day, but secretly each of them knew what the *real* treasure was. The real treasure of the vineyard lay in the grapes and wine. The real treasure came with hard work.

In the end the brothers discovered that hard work, not luck or laziness, earned them their wealth. Their father was very wise when he thought of the plan that would make his sons work hard.

At school, we have the chance to work hard. It's up to us to use that chance well and to do our best.

Prayer
Thank you God, for all the hard work we've done this year. Thank you for the opportunity to work hard. Thank you for the ability to work hard. Help us always to do our best.

Amen

Hymn
'Hands to work and feet to run' *Someone's singing, Lord*

Building blocks
Week 12 Endings

If you have a *very* good memory, you might remember our first assembly of this school year. It was a long time ago! It was last September at the very beginning of the school year. Now we are at the end of the school year; today is our last day.

That first assembly was about a boy called Jim. He'd just moved into a new class, but he didn't expect to do very well. He thought he was quite naughty because he seemed always to be getting into trouble. But Jim's new teacher gave him jobs to do. She gave him new responsibilities and he grew into those responsibilities.

What about *you* this year? Have you grown into *your* responsibilities? Looking around, I can see lots of you who have.

Responsible, sensible, hard-working children, who always try to do their best, make our school into the good place it is.

This morning, instead of telling you a story, I'm going to ask the children who are leaving our school today, to come and write something on these building blocks. I'd like them to write something they want to say thank you for. They might want to say thank you for a friend, or school dinners, or fun, or a trip out. They might want to say thank you for something they've learned, or for some first-aid when they fell.

We'll see what they put.

As each brick is written, I'm going to ask the children to build them, here, into a wall. They'll need to remember to position their bricks so that you can read their words.

And there is our wall. It's a strong wall with a great many thank-yous in it. Each brick represents something that's good about our school. These are the foundations that make our school strong. And you can see from the bricks, that everyone helps build our school into what it is. Our school wouldn't be a school without us, it's family.

I hope the children who are leaving us today will use their good foundations well, to build on in their lives as they grow older. I hope you all remember the foundations you have built at our school this year.

Prayer
Thank you God, for our school year. Thank you for the friends we have made, the fun we've had, the new things we've learned. Thank you for the good foundations we have made, and help us to build on them in the future.

Amen

Hymn
'The building song' *Come and Praise*, Vol 1

Practical ideas
This assembly, though simple, is visually effective. The size of the wall can be determined by:

a) how many infant building blocks are available,
b) how many leaving children there are.

If there is a large number of children, representatives from each class can be chosen; if there are few leavers, they can write several blocks each.

The assembly is more successful if the older children have time to prepare, and to decide what they are to write.

The simplest way to write the bricks, is to prepare several pieces of thin card, each cut to the size of a brick side. These can be blu-tacked or sellotaped to the bricks in advance. The children should write in large clear lettering, using felt marker pens, so that everyone assembled can see the words.

Alphabetical index of stories

Advent ring, The 57
April Fool's Day 140

Balloons 81
Bee who wanted to be different, The 35
Best gold, The 45
Birthday party, The 99
Building blocks 236
Bumble bee, The 15

Calm blue sea, A 225
Candlemas Day 100
Certificate, The 87
Christopher wins a gold 219
Cluttered room, The 72
Comic Relief Day 137
Computer genius and the dustbinman, The 12
Cormorant, The 38
Corn dollies 22
Cornelia's treasure 47
Cow, a lioness and a jackal, A 184
Crocodile tears 118

Donkey and the dog, The 6
Dragon and the dark, The 104

Eagle and the jackdaw, The 10
Eggs around the world 154

Factory and the hospital, The   204
Fair king, The   175
Fair's fair   31
Feeding of the five thousand, The   122
First Whit Sunday, The   193
Five rabbits   116
Flowers for a Duchess   27
Follow the star   74
Fox and the cockerel, The   163

Good kings, The   59
Good Samaritan, The   135
Guardsman and his horse, The   2

Hannah Hauxwell   70
Hard work   235
Harvest festival – Bread   17
Hetain's promise   112
Hunter, The   208

Jersey cow, The   173
Jim   1

Last leaf, The   189
Legend of the bells, The   152
Legend of the Easter rabbit, The   156
Lion and the hare, The   130
Listening tree, The   114
Lost magic, The   8

Malin and Bon   63
Man and his goat, The   171
Man and his neighbour, A   132
Man who day-dreamed, The   164
Man who walked to Warsaw, The   168
Maypole dancers, The   182
Midsummer Night's Dream, A   217
Monkey and the bridge, The   29
Monsieur Jean's carnations   119
Months of the year, The   83
Mothering Sunday   150
Mountain rescue   228

Mrs Edwards and the sewing machine 42
Mrs Hetherington 61
Mrs Robinson and Mrs Clegg 191

Nasrudin and the donkeys 202
New baby, The 94
Not everyone can win 144
Notices, The 206

Packman, The 195
Pancake Day 121
Paper birds, The 89
Peregrine falcons 146
Pied Piper, The 107
Plough Monday 85
Prince Radleigh's second holiday 230
Problem field, The 129

Rogationtide 180

School trip, The 212
Singh – as brave as a lion 166
Skip-a-snack 20
Slide, The 68
Something old, something new 4
Sowing seeds 148
Sports' Day 221
St Catherine's Day 52
St Swithin 233
Star is Bjorn, A 223
Stir up Sunday 54
Story about nobody, A 26
Story of book tokens, The 210
Story of cornflakes, The 124
Strawberry-coloured cow, The 49
Stupid monkeys, The 127

Three bears 33
Three fish, The 187
Three frogs 91
Three things 40
To Egypt 75

Toy kangaroo, The   142
Two brothers, The   14
Two girls and a box of matches   161
Two princes go to market   102

Urashima   109

Village church, The   95

Whitsuntide clothes, The   197
Woman and a dog, A   215
Woman and the three loaves of bread, The   177
Wren, The   66

Theme index *(other than main themes listed in contents)*

Animal stories
The guardsman and his horse   2
The donkey and the dog   6
The eagle and the jackdaw   10
The bumble bee   15
The monkey and the bridge   29
Three bears   33
The bee who wanted to be different   35
The cormorant   38
The strawberry-coloured cow   49
The wren   66
To Egypt   75
Three frogs   91
Candlemas Day   100
The Pied Piper   107
Five rabbits   116
Crocodile tears   118
The stupid monkeys   127
The lion and the hare   130
Peregrine falcons   146
The legend of the Easter rabbit   156
The fox and the cockerel   163
The man and his goat   171
The Jersey cow   173
A cow, a lioness and a jackal   184
Nasrudin and the donkeys   202
The hunter   208
A woman and a dog   215

Caring for the environment/things
The guardsman and his horse   2
Something old, something new   4
The cormorant   38
Three things   40
The listening tree   114
The problem field   129
The man and his neighbour   132
Peregrine falcons   146
Two girls and a box of matches   161
Rogationtide   180
The hunter   208
Hard work   235

Caring for people
The two brothers   14
Skip-a-snack   20
The monkey and the bridge   29
Three bears   33
Mrs Edwards and the sewing machine   42
Cornelia's treasure   47
St Catherine's Day   52
The good kings   59
Mrs Hetherington   61
Malin and Bon   63
The slide   68
The new baby   94
The birthday party   97
Hetain's promise   112
The listening tree   114
The feeding of the five thousand   122
The story of cornflakes   124
The good Samaritan   135
Comic Relief Day   137
April Fool's Day   140
Mothering Sunday   150
Two girls and a box of matches   161
The fair king   175
The woman and the three loaves of bread   177
A cow, a lioness and a jackal   184
The last leaf   189
Mrs Robinson and Mrs Clegg   191

The factory and the hospital   **204**
A woman and a dog   **215**
A calm blue sea   **225**
Mountain rescue   **228**
Prince Radleigh's second holiday   **230**

Cheerfulness
Corn dollies   **22**
Hannah Hauxwell   **70**
Balloons   **81**
The paper birds   **89**
The woman and the three loaves of bread   **177**
Mrs Robinson and Mrs Clegg   **191**
The school trip   **212**
Prince Radleigh's second holiday   **230**

Co-operation
The computer genius and the dustbinman   **12**
Corn dollies   **22**
A story about nobody   **26**
Three bears   **33**
The bee who wanted to be different   **35**
The good kings   **59**
The months of the year   **83**
The village church   **95**
Two princes go to market   **102**
The problem field   **129**
The toy kangaroo   **142**
Mothering Sunday   **150**
Eggs around the world   **154**
The maypole dancers   **182**
A cow, a lioness and a jackal   **184**
The school trip   **212**
A Midsummer Night's Dream   **217**
Prince Radleigh's second holiday   **230**
Hard work   **235**
Building blocks   **236**

Courage
The monkey and the bridge   **29**
Three bears   **33**
Cornelia's treasure   **47**

The slide   68
Hannah Hauxwell   70
The paper birds   89
The dragon and the dark   104
Singh – as brave as a lion   166
The last leaf   189
The packman   195
Mountain rescue   228

Doing your best
   Jim   1
   Corn dollies   22
   Flowers for a Duchess   27
   Cornelia's treasure   47
   The wren   66
   Hannah Hauxwell   70
   The certificate   87
   Three frogs   91
   Two princes go to market   102
   Not everyone can win   144
   The legend of the Easter rabbit   156
   Rogationtide   180
   The last leaf   189
   The story of book tokens   210
   A woman and a dog   215
   Christopher wins a gold   219
   A star is Bjorn   223
   Hard work   235

Forgiveness
   Three things   40
   A man and his neighbour   132
   April Fool's Day   140
   The packman   195
   A woman and a dog   215
   A Midsummer Night's Dream   217

Generosity
   Skip-a-snack   20
   The strawberry-coloured cow   49
   Follow the star   74
   The feeding of the five thousand   122

The story of cornflakes 124
The toy kangaroo 142
The woman and the three loaves of bread 177
The last leaf 189
Mrs Robinson and Mrs Clegg 191
The school trip 212
A woman and a dog 215

Greed
Something old, something new 4
Fair's fair 31
The best gold 45
The strawberry-coloured cow 49
Malin and Bon 63
To Egypt 75
A man and his neighbour 132
The man who walked to Warsaw 168
The man and his goat 171
The three fish 187
The packman 195
Sports Day 221
Mountain rescue 228

Helpfulness
Jim 1
Skip-a-snack 20
Flowers for a Duchess 27
Three bears 33
Mrs Hetherington 61
The months of the year 83
The dragon and the dark 104
Pancake Day 121
April Fool's Day 140
Mothering Sunday 150
The fair king 175
The woman and the three loaves of bread 177
Rogationtide 180
The last leaf 189
Monsieur Jean's carnations 199
The factory and the hospital 204
The notices 206
The story of book tokens 210

The school trip   212
A woman and a dog   215
A calm blue sea   225
Mountain rescue   228
Prince Radleigh's second holiday   230

Honesty
The lost magic   8
The eagle and the jackdaw   10
Fair's fair   31
Malin and Bon   63
The Pied Piper   107
Crocodile tears   118
A man and his neighbour   132
The man and his goat   171
A cow, a lioness and a jackdaw   184
Nasrudin and the donkeys   202
Sports Day   221

Humility
The lost magic   8
Hannah Hauxwell   70
The fair king   175
St Swithin   233

Kindness
Three bears   33
The strawberry-coloured cow   49
The good kings   59
The good Samaritan   135
April Fool's Day   140
The toy kangaroo   142
Not everyone can win   144
The Jersey cow   173
The woman and the three loaves of bread   177
The last leaf   189
Mrs Robinson and Mrs Clegg   191
The school trip   212
A woman and a dog   215

Loyalty
Three bears   33

Cornelia's treasure 47
Malin and Bon 63
Singh – as brave as a lion 166
A cow, a lioness and a jackal 184
The last leaf 189
Mountain rescue 228

Obedience
The wren 66
Five rabbits 116
Crocodile tears 118
The maypole dancers 182
Mountain rescue 228
Hard work 235

Patience
The good kings 59
The wren 66
The months of the year 83
The certificate 87
The paper birds 89
Three frogs 91
Hetain's promise 112
The legend of the bells 152
The fair king 175
The Whitsuntide clothes 197
Christopher wins a gold 219
Hard work 235

Perseverance
The bumble bee 15
Corn dollies 22
The certificate 87
The paper birds 89
Three frogs 91
The story of cornflakes 124
The toy kangaroo 142
The legend of the Easter rabbit 156
The Jersey cow 173
The fair king 175
Christopher wins a gold 219
A star is Bjorn 223

Hard work   235

Responsibility
   Jim   1
   Corn dollies   22
   A story about nobody   26
   Flowers for a Duchess   27
   The monkey and the bridge   29
   Three bears   33
   Mrs Edwards and the sewing machine   42
   Cornelia's treasure   47
   The slide   68
   Five rabbits   116
   The stupid monkeys   127
   Peregrine falcons   146
   Two girls and a box of matches   161
   The factory and the hospital   204
   The notices   206
   The hunter   208
   A woman and a dog   215
   A calm blue sea   225
   Mountain rescue   228

Selfishness
   Fair's fair   31
   The bee who wanted to be different   35
   The listening tree   114
   Mothering Sunday   150
   The man who walked to Warsaw   168
   The three fish   187
   Sports Day   221
   A calm blue sea   225
   Mountain rescue   228

Sharing
   The guardsman and his horse   2
   Skip-a-snack   20
   Corn dollies   22
   A story about nobody   26
   Mrs Hetherington   61
   Malin and Bon   63
   The village church   95

Pancake Day   121
The feeding of the five thousand   122
The story of cornflakes   124
The problem field   129
Peregrine falcons   146
Eggs around the world   154
The fair king   175
The woman and the three loaves of bread   177
Rogationtide   180
The maypole dancers   182
The three fish   187
The last leaf   189
Mrs Robinson and Mrs Clegg   191
The school trip   212
A woman and a dog   215
Prince Radleigh's second holiday   230
Building blocks   236

Stories from the major religions
Buddhism
    The lost magic   8
    The monkey and the bridge   29
    The good kings   59
    The stupid monkeys   127
    A cow, a lioness and a jackal   184
Christianity
    St Catherine's Day   52
    The Advent ring   57
    Follow the star   74
    To Egypt   75
    The feeding of the five thousand   122
    The good Samaritan   135
    Sowing seeds   148
    The first Whit Sunday   193
Hinduism
    Malin and Bon   63
    The lion and the hare   130
    A man and his neighbour   132
    The man who day-dreamed   164
    The man and his goat   171
Islam
    The fair king   175

Nasrudin and the donkeys   202
The hunter   208
A woman and a dog   215
Judaism
The cluttered room   72
The man who walked to Warsaw   168
The woman and the three loaves of bread   177
Sikhism
Singh – as brave as a lion   166

Thanksgiving
Harvest festival – Bread   17
Corn dollies   22
The story of cornflakes   124
Rogationtide   180
The story of book tokens   210

Thinking
Three bears   35
Cornelia's treasure   47
St Catherine's Day   52
The birthday party   97
The dragon and the dark   104
Crocodile tears   118
Comic Relief Day   137
Mothering Sunday   150
Two girls and a box of matches   161
The man and his goat   171
The fair king   175
Rogationtide   180
The maypole dancers   182
The hunter   208
The story of book tokens   210
The school trip   212
A woman and a dog   215
A star is Bjorn   223
A calm blue sea   225
Mountain rescue   228

True stories
Skip-a-snack   20
Corn dollies   22

Flowers for a Duchess 27
The cormorant 38
St Catherine's Day 52
Stir-up Sunday 54
Hannah Hauxwell 70
Plough Monday 85
The paper birds 89
Pancake Day 121
The story of cornflakes 124
Comic Relief Day 137
April Fool's Day 140
The toy kangaroo 142
Peregrine falcons 146
Eggs around the world 154
Two girls and a box of matches 161
The Whitsuntide clothes 197
The notices 206
The story of book tokens 210
Christoper wins a gold 219
A star is Bjorn 223
A calm blue sea 225
Mountain rescue 228

Working together
The guardsman and his horse 2
Skip-a-snack 20
Corn dollies 22
A story about nobody 26
The bee who wanted to be different 35
Cornelia's treasure 47
Mrs Hetherington 61
The village church 95
Two princes go to market 102
The problem field 129
The toy kangaroo 142
Mothering Sunday 150
Eggs around the world 154
The fair king 175
Rogationtide 180
The maypole dancers 182
Mrs Robinson and Mrs Clegg 191
Monsieur Jean's carnations 199

The school trip   212
Prince Radleigh's second holiday   230
Hard work   235
Building blocks   236